My Disney
STARS AND HEROES 3

Workbook with eBook

Catherine Zgouras

LESSONS 1 and 2

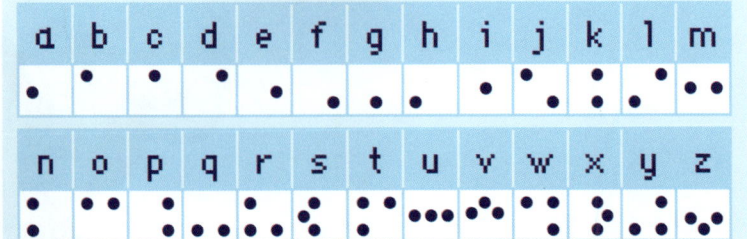

Welcome!

1 ✏️ **Find and write. Then match.**

1. I live in a small t   o   w   n .

2. Our __ __ __ __ has big, red buses and trams.

3. My __ __ __ __ __ __ __ doesn't have a school.

4. You can see animals in the __ __ __ __ __ __ __ __ __ __ .

2 ✏️ **Put the words in order to make questions. Then answer for you.**

1. you / Where / do / live?

   _____

   I live _____ .

   Me: _____

2. you / Do / in / live / the / countryside?

   _____

   _____

   No, _____ .

   Me: _____

I can name places and write about where people live.

LESSONS 3 and 4

1 Look, choose, and write.

Argentina   China   India   Mexico   Turkey   the United Kingdom

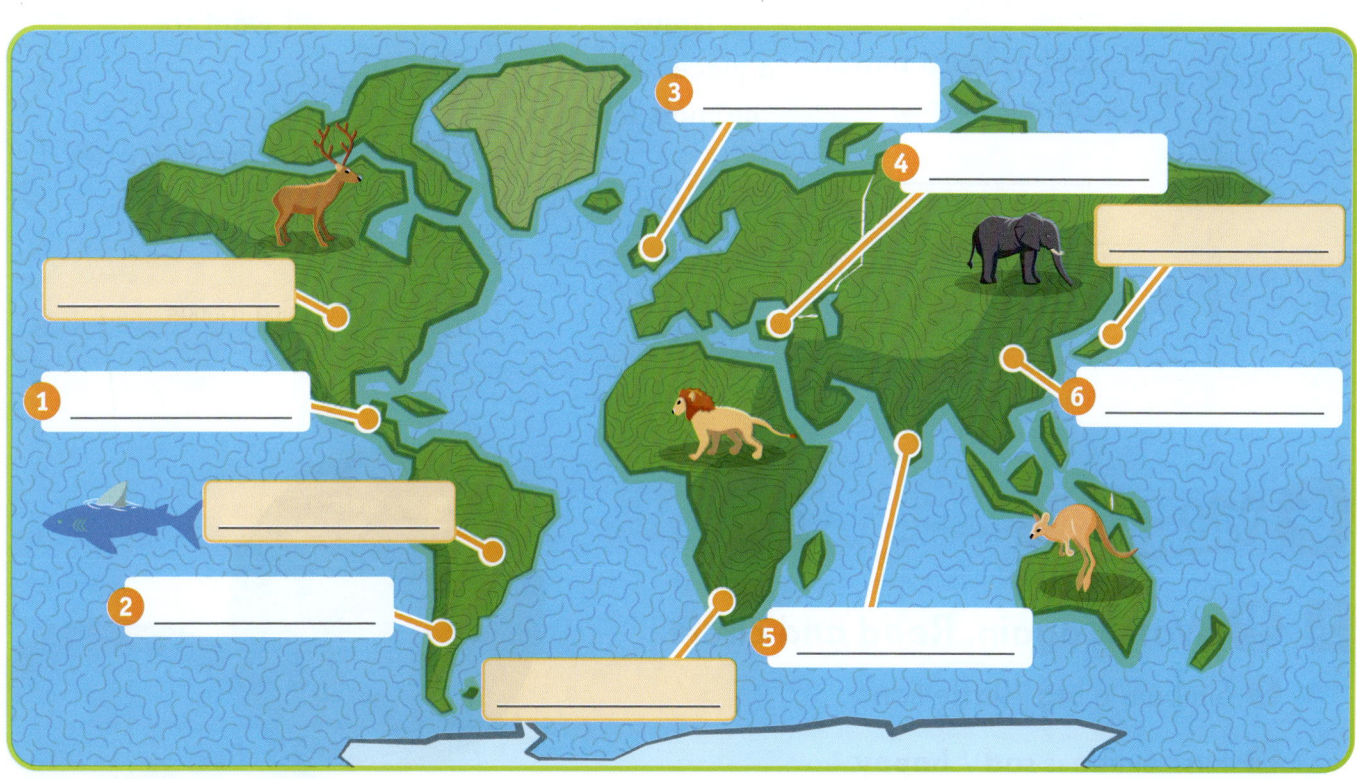

2 Read the story again and complete. Then write the countries on the map.

1. Where is Sato ___from___ ?
   She's from ___Japan___ .

2. _____ is Uma's mom from?
   _____ South Africa.

3. Where is Diego's dad from?
   _____

4. _____ Max from?
   _____

3 Answer for you. Then write the countries on the map.

Talk to a new friend. How are you the same? How are you different?

Where are you from? _____

_____? My mom / dad is from _____.

Where are your grandparents from? _____

_____? My friend is from _____.

I can name countries.

1 Animal friends

Learning Heroes

I want to learn new animal words:

_____
_____
_____

Draw:
a place where animals live

I want to:
 a story
 about animals and their bodies
 The Lion King video
 about helping friends

Video quiz

1  Watch again. Read and circle.

1. Simba is a **big** / **little** lion.
2. First, Simba is **sad** / **happy**.
3. Timon and Pumba sing **birds** / **songs** to Simba.
4. The animals **play games** / **fly** together.
5. When Simba is a big lion, he **helps** / **doesn't help** his friends.

2 Choose and write. Then complete for you.

Simba   Timon and Pumbaa

1. _____ help Simba. They stop the birds.
2. _____ helps Pumbaa and Timon. He stops Nala.
3. My friends help me with _____.
4. I help my friends with _____.

LESSON 1 Vocabulary

3 Look, circle, and write.

m e e r k a t r h i n o g i r a f f e h y e n a

1 _____

2 _____

3 _____

4 ___meerkat___

Challenge!
Find 6 letters in orange. Then guess the word. _____

4 Look at 3. Read and write.

1 It doesn't sit. It stands up. It's small.

It's a ___meerkat___ .

2 It's isn't big. It's fast and gray.

It's a _____ .

3 It's big and gray. It's isn't tall.

It's a _____ .

4 It isn't gray. It isn't small. It's brown and tall.

It's a _____ .

Extra time?

Write two sentences to describe your favorite animal.

 I can name animals.

LESSON 2
Vocabulary

1 Look and match.

1. brown fur
2. yellow wing
3. black claws
4. brown tail
5. yellow feathers
6. gray horn
7. gray trunk
8. black beak

2 Look, read, and write.

1. This is my cat. It has ___claws___ and black ___fur___ .

2. It's a chicken. It has two _____ and white _____ .

3. Look at this elephant. It has a long _____ and a short _____ .

4. This is a duck. It has a big yellow _____ .

5. This rhino is strong. It has two _____ .

Find out!
How many white rhinos are there in the world today? Why?

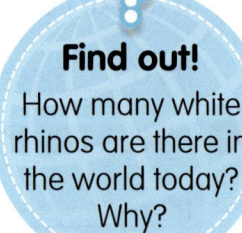

Extra time?
Make lists of animals you know with tails, with horns, and with fur.

I can name animal body parts.

LESSON 3
Grammar

1 🎧 **Listen and match.**

1. Zazu is a bird. He uses
2. Timon is a meerkat. He uses
3. Shenzi is a hyena. She uses
4. Nala is a lion. She uses

her ears   his legs   her claws   his wings

to climb trees.   to stand up.   to fly.   to find her friends.

Grammar Heroes

🧩 **Read and write.**

Simba uses ⊃⊂ his _____ to climb.

Monkeys _____ ⊃⊂ _____ _____ to keep warm.

2 **Imagine you are an animal. Write and draw.**

I'm a _____ . I use my _____ .

Extra time?
Write about you.
I use my mouth to eat.

I can talk about what body parts animals use to do actions.

Animal dress-up

  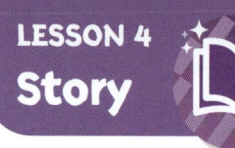

LESSON 4
Story

1 Remember the story. Circle *T* (True) or *F* (False).
1. The children play dress-up.   (T) / F
2. Uma is a tree.   T / F
3. Max uses his trunk to drink water.   T / F
4. Sato can fly with her wings.   T / F

2 Look, read, and match.

1 — c

a) I use my wings to fly! I'm flying in the sky.

b) I want to be a giraffe! It has a long neck.

c) I use my claws to climb! I'm climbing a tall tree in the forest.

d) I use my trunk to drink! I drink water.

3 Read and write. Then compare with a friend.

1. Diego can't play with his friends.
   How does he feel?
   __He feels sad.__
   What does Max do?
   _____
   What does Max say?
   _____

2. One of your friends can't play with you.
   How do you think your friend feels?
   _____
   What do you do?
   _____
   What do you say?
   _____

My favorite scene in the story is number ___ because _____.

Extra time?
Create an animal costume and describe it.

I **can** read a story about helping a friend.

8

LESSON 5
Vocabulary and Grammar

1 Look and find the animal. Then choose and write.

~~desert~~ forest grassland lake ocean river

1 The meerkat is in the ____desert____ .
2 I can see a dolphin in the _____ .
3 There's a rhino in the _____ .
4 The frog is in the _____ .
5 There's a giraffe in the _____ .
6 Can you see the lizard in the _____ ?

2 Put the words in order to make questions. Then match.

1 Where / live / do / snakes / ?
  Where do snakes live? _____

2 do / What / eat / lions / ?
  _____

3 have / do / birds / What / ?
  _____

a They eat meat.

b They have wings.

c They live in the forest.

3 Look, read, and write.

1 ____Where____ do ____rhinos____ live?
  They _____ in the _____ .
2 What _____ rhinos _____ ?
  _____ have _____ .
3 _____ do lions _____ ?
  _____ eat _____ .
4 What _____ lions _____ ?
  _____ tails, fur, and claws.

Extra time?
Make a list of animals you know.

 talk about where animals live.

9

LESSON 6
Listening and Speaking

1 🎧 **Listen and circle.**

1 Giraffes

They drink water from **snakes** / **lakes**.

They eat **pasta** / **leaves** and grass.

They use their **necks** / **knees** to eat leaves from tall trees.

2 Hyenas

They live in the **farm** / **forest** and in the grassland.

They have **fur** / **hair** and claws.

They use their claws to eat **leaves** / **meat**.

2 Look, read, and complete the fact file.

Meerkats

Meerkats have fur and a tail. They use their tail to stand up. They eat fruit, insects, and snakes. They live in the desert and in the grassland.

Animal: _____

Live: _____

Eat: _____

Fact: _____

3 💬 **Think of an animal. Write and draw. Then answer.**

Animal: _____

Live: _____

Eat: _____

Fact: _____

Where do they live?

⏰ **Extra time?**

Think of an animal. A friend asks you three questions to guess the animal.

 use fact files to talk about animals.

LESSON 7
Myself and others
Social awareness

Helping your friends

1 Read and check (✓).

Are you helping your friends?

	Yes	No
1 Adam doesn't understand a game you are playing. You explain the game.	○	○
2 Ania doesn't have colored pencils. She can't draw. You don't share your pencils.	○	○
3 Kim's bag is heavy. You help her with her bag.	○	○
4 The new boy in class doesn't have any friends. You talk to him.	○	○

2 Read and write.

1. How do you help your friends in class? _____
2. How do you help your friends at recess? _____
3. How do you help your friends on the weekend? _____
4. What do you say to your friends to help them? _____

My portfolio

3 How do you help your friends? Draw and write.

My helping hand

in class

at recess

at lunch

after school

on the weekend

Be a hero!
How can you help your friends this week? Say.

I can recognize how I can help my friends.

Science — The food chain

LESSON 8 — My world

1 Read, look, and match.

1. The sun makes plants grow.
2. Plants grow from seeds.
3. Insects eat the leaves on plants.
4. Birds eat insects and fruit.
5. Lions eat meat and they like to eat birds.

 1
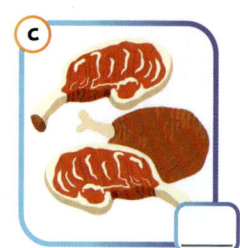

2 Look, think, and number in order.

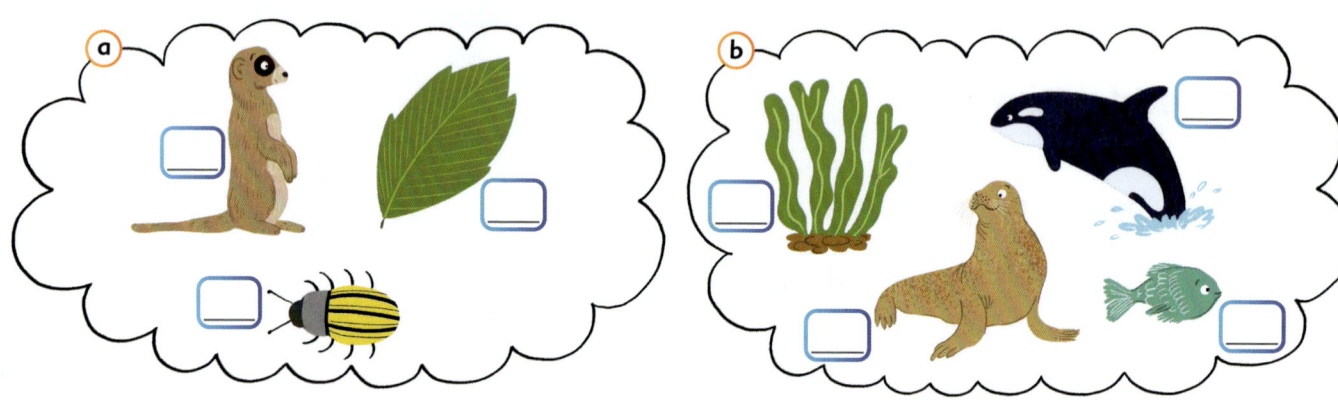

3 Which animal can be at the top of food chain 1? Complete food chain 2 with your own ideas.

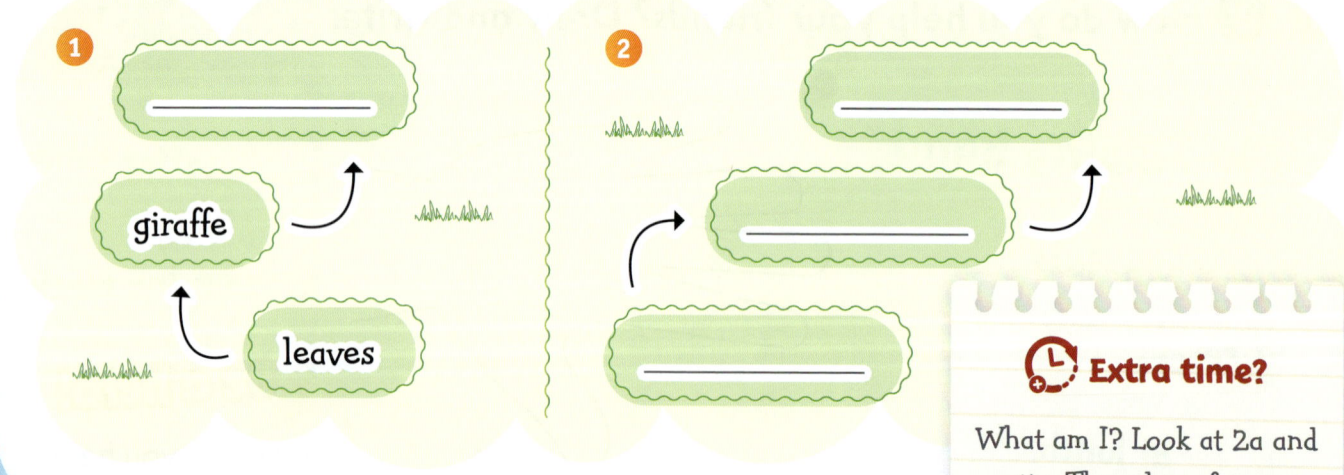

I can read and talk about food chains.

Extra time? What am I? Look at 2a and write. Then draw for your friend to guess.

A food chain poster

LESSON 9 Project

1 Plan your food chain poster.

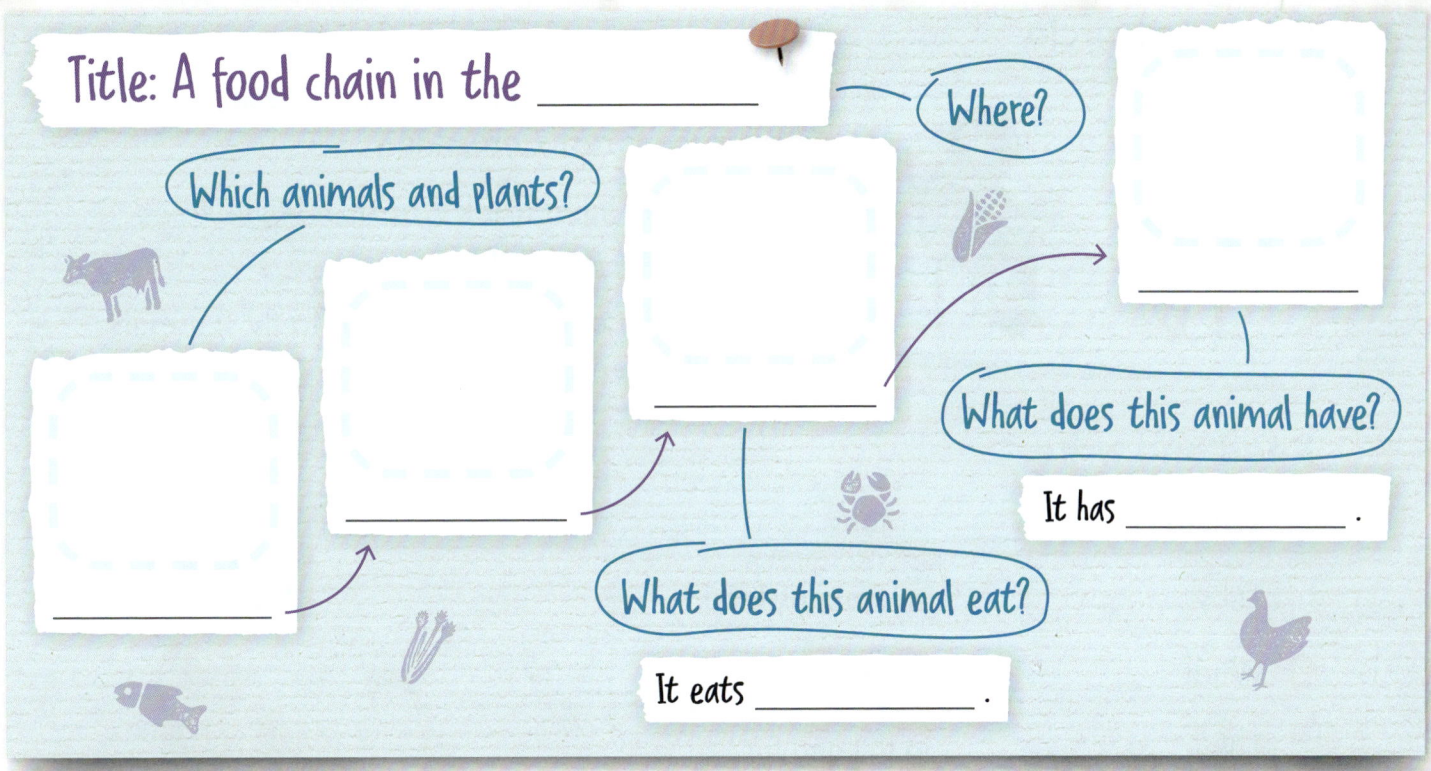

Title: A food chain in the _____

Where?

Which animals and plants?

What does this animal have?

It has _____ .

What does this animal eat?

It eats _____ .

2 Write your presentation. Then practice with a friend.

Hello, I'd like to tell you about my food chain.

The sun _____ .

The _____ eats _____ . It uses _____ .

The _____ eats _____ . It uses _____ .

We're all part of the same circle of life.

_____ . Does anyone have any _____ ?

Check!

There are headings and pictures in my poster. ○

There are words next to the pictures. ○

3 Reflect on your project.

I answered all questions from the class:

I finish by asking for questions:

My food chain poster

What animals are in your food chain? _____

Are there headings on your poster? _____

Are there pictures with words? _____

I can make and present a food chain poster.

13

My progress journal

**LESSON 10
Review**

1 Read and circle.

1. A **giraffe** / **hyena** has a long neck. It lives in the **forest** / **grassland**.
2. A rhino has a **trunk** / **horn**. It swims in **a lake** / **an ocean**.
3. A bird uses its **claws** / **wings** to fly. It uses its **tail** / **beak** to eat.

2 Read and write.

1. Where ____do____ lions ____live____ ?
   They _____ in the grassland.
2. What _____ hyenas _____ ?
   They _____ a tail and fur.
3. What _____ birds _____ ?
   They _____ wings and feathers.

3 What I know.

Write. What's your favorite animal from this unit?

_____

Say. Talk about this scene from the video.
What happens? Do you like it?

Star progress

- This unit was ☆☆☆☆☆
- My favorite lesson is _____
  because _____ .
- I can now _____ .

UNIT 1
Exam practice

Listening

1 🎧 1.3 **Listen, color, and write.**

Reading and Writing

2 **Read and choose.**

1. What do meerkats eat?
   - (a) They eat insects.
   - (b) I like meerkats.
   - (c) Yes, they do.

2. What do lions have?
   - (a) They eat meat.
   - (b) They have fur.
   - (c) No, they haven't.

3. Where do birds live?
   - (a) They have wings.
   - (b) No, they don't.
   - (c) They live in the forest.

4. Where do rhinos live?
   - (a) They live in the grassland.
   - (b) They have four legs.
   - (c) Yes, they do.

Speaking

3 💬 **Look at the pictures in 1 and in 3. Say what is different.**

In 1 the monkey is using its hands to climb.

In 3 the monkey is using its tail to climb.

15

2 Student life

Learning Heroes

I want to learn new words for school classes:

_____
_____
_____

Draw: a school club

I want to:
 a story
 about school clubs
 Monsters University video
 about working in a team

1 Watch again. Circle *T* (True) or *F* (False).
1. Some monsters are in school clubs. **T** / F
2. Mike and Sulley are not on the same team. T / F
3. Mike is in the Scare Games. T / F
4. The OKs aren't fast in the first race. T / F
5. Mike and Sulley are first in the next race. T / F

2 Read and circle. Then write for you.
1. What do the OKs do in the first race?
   They **work** / **don't work** together.
2. What do the OKs do in the second race?
   They **work** / **don't work** as a team.
3. What teams are you in?
   _____

LESSON 1 **Vocabulary**

3 Follow and write.

1. c o o k i n g club
2. _ _ _ _ _ club
3. _ _ _ _ club
4. _ _ _ _ _ _ club

4 Read and write.

1. I read and talk about books at ____book club____ .
2. I play table tennis and soccer at _____ .
3. I can make cakes at _____ .
4. I can dance to music at _____ .

Challenge!
What's the secret word?

Sulley k _ _ _ _ a ball playing soccer at sports club.

Extra time?
Make lists of sports you play in sports club and things you cook in cooking club.

I can name school clubs.

LESSON 2
Vocabulary

1 Look, read, and match.

1. This is math class. `e`
2. It's science class. ☐
3. This is English class. ☐
4. It's music class. ☐
5. They're in P.E. ☐
6. This is history class. ☐
7. This is geography class. ☐
8. They are in art class. ☐

2 Read and write. Then draw 🙂 or ☹ for you.

1. We're singing. We're in ____music____ class.
2. I'm writing numbers. I'm in _____ class.
3. We're playing basketball. We're in _____ .
4. I'm painting a tree. I'm in _____ class.
5. I'm learning about the past in _____ .
6. We're learning new words in _____ .
7. We're looking at a big map in _____ .

The missing class is _____ .

Find out!
How many languages do people speak in your country? Which languages are they?

Extra time?
Imagine you are in your favorite class. What class is it? What are you doing?

I can name school classes.

LESSON 3
Grammar

1 🎧 2.1 **Listen and check (✓).**

Grammar Heroes

Read and write.

What time _____ the team race start?

It _____ five to four.

2 **Read and answer for you.**

① What time does your English class start?

It starts at _____.

② What time do you arrive at school?

_____

③ What time do you leave school?

_____

④ What time does your math class finish?

_____

⏱ Extra time?

Look at 2. Ask and answer.

I can say what time things start and finish.

Our amazing den

LESSON 4 Story

1 Remember the story. Look, read, and match.

a. What a great team!

b. It's OK. I can fix that. We have to work together.

c. Oh, no! We can't build our den now.

d. The children are working together to build their den.

2 Read and circle.

1. The children have **science** / **P.E.**

2. Uma and Diego **don't work** / **work** together at the beginning.

3. Uma **gives** / **doesn't give** Diego her stick.

4. The children are having fun in the **den** / **art class** at the end.

3 Read and write. Then compare with a friend.

① At the beginning, Uma and Diego don't work together as a team.

Are they happy at the beginning?

No, they aren't.

What does Sato do?

_____

What does Uma say?

_____

Are they happy at the end?

_____

② Imagine you're building a den with some friends. Two friends aren't working together as a team.

Are you and your friends happy at the beginning?

_____

What do you do?

_____

What do you say?

_____

Are you and your friends happy at the end?

_____

I think the story is _____ because _____.

I can read a story about working as a team.

Extra time?

Think about how you can make a forest den. Draw and write instructions.

LESSON 5
Vocabulary and Grammar

1 **Look, choose, and write.** cafeteria computer lab gym library ~~science lab~~ sports field

1. science lab
2. _____
3. _____
4. _____
5. _____
6. _____

2 **Put the words in order to make a question. Then read and put a ✔ or ✘.**

1. to / the / cafeteria / get / How / do / you / ?

    How do you get to the cafeteria?

    Turn right.   ◯

2. you / get / How / do / the / to / science lab / ?

    _____

    Go straight, then turn left.   ◯

3 **Look at 1 and write. Then write one more question and answer.**

1. __How do__ you __get__ to the gym? Go straight, then turn right.
2. How do you get to the sports field? _____ right.
3. _____ library? _____
4. _____ _____

Extra time?

What's your favorite place in your school? How do you get there?

 talk about how to get to places in my school.

21

LESSON 6
Listening and Speaking

1 🎧 **Listen and match.**

① library   ② sports field   ③ computer lab

a

c

b

2 Read, choose, and write.

get   right   left   ~~school~~   straight

Eve: Hi! I'm new at the **1** ___school___ .
Can you help me, please?

Marcus: Hi! Yes, of course.

Eve: My class is in the gym.
How do you **2** _____ there?

Marcus: Go **3** _____ and turn **4** _____ .
Then turn **5** _____ .

Eve: Great! Thank you!

3 💬 **Read, choose, and complete. Then ask and answer with a friend.**

~~music room~~   computer lab   gym   cafeteria

Can you help me?

Yes, of course.

How do you get to the _____ ?

Go straight and then turn right.

Great! Thank you!

⏰ Extra time?

Write directions to your favorite place in school. Can your friends guess the place?

I can use a school map to say how to get to places.

Working as a team

**LESSON 7
Myself and others**
Relationship skills

1 Read and check (✓). Then complete.

	Work as a team	Don't work as a team
talk to others	✓	
don't listen to others		
help others		
don't share ideas		
_____		
_____		

2 Make a team and work together. Do the team challenge!

Think of a team name: _____

Choose one challenging thing you all want to do. _____

Look at 1 and find strategies that can help with activity 3.

My portfolio

3 Design a team T-shirt. Use your ideas from 1 and 2.

Be a hero!
How can you solve problems as a team?

I can work in a team.

Green energy

**LESSON 8
My world**

1 Read, choose, and write.

coal   energy   oil   sunlight

1. Things like televisions and computers work with _____ .
2. _____ and _____ are bad because they make the air dirty.
3. Energy from _____ is good for our planet because it's clean.

2 What energy do they show? Look and circle.

This energy is from **coal / water**. It **is / isn't** green energy.

This is energy from **oil / wind**. This **is / isn't** green energy.

This is energy from **sunlight / coal**. This **is / isn't** green energy.

This is energy from **wind / coal**. This **is / isn't** green energy.

3 Find out about something that uses green energy. Draw and write.

This is _____ . It uses green energy from _____ .

I can read and talk about energy.

Extra time?

Think of your home. What objects can use green energy? Write.

An "ideal school" brochure

LESSON 9 Project

1 Work in groups. Write your ideas.

Student A: clubs
_____
_____

Student B: classes
_____
_____

Student C: places
_____
_____

Student D: energy
_____
_____

2 Make your brochure. Write and draw.

Our ideal school

Clubs: _____

Classes: _____

When: _____

Places: _____

Map of the school

Energy from _____

At our school we want _____ .

We want to have _____ .

The _____ is next to the _____ .

We use energy from _____ .

Check!

There are pictures with arrows and words. ◯

There are headings and sentences. ◯

3 Reflect on your project.

We divided up tasks to work better:

I share my ideas with my group:

My ideal school brochure

Does your ideal school sound great? _____

Do you like your brochure? Why? _____

I can work in a group to create a brochure for my ideal school.

**LESSON 10
Review**

My progress journal

1 **Read and circle.**
1. I love reading. I'm joining the **cooking** / **book** club.
2. The library is next to the **sports** / **math** field.
3. I like doing experiments in the **gym** / **science lab**.
4. Our **cafeteria** / **math class** starts at quarter to nine.
5. The children leave school at four **thirty** / **thirteen**.

2 **Read, choose, and write.**

How   ~~music~~   right   sports club   straight   three thirty   turn

Elena, what's your favorite class?
It's 1 ___music___ . I love playing the drums.

Do you go to a club?
Yes, I do. I go to a 2 _____ .

What time does P.E. start?
It starts at 3 _____ .

How do you get to the gym?
Go 4 _____ , then 5 _____ left.

6 _____ do we get to the cafeteria?
It's there. Turn left.

3 **What I know.**

Write. What are your favorite classes? _____

Say. Talk about this scene from the video.
What happens? Do you like it?

Star progress
- This unit was ☆☆☆☆☆
- My favorite lesson is _____
  because _____ .
- I can now _____ .

UNIT 2
Exam practice

Listening

1 🎧 2.3 **Listen and check (✓).**

1. Which club does Jack want to join?

2. Where's the library?
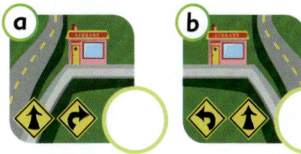

3. What time does Peter's English class start?
  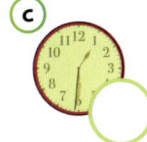

4. Where's Lily at 11 o'clock?

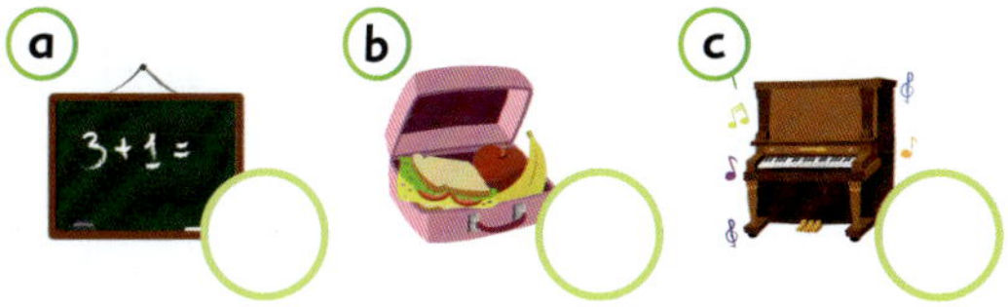

Reading and Writing

2 **Read, choose, and write.**

I like school. I have my math class at nine **1** _o'clock_ in the morning. Then history starts at **2** _____ ten. In the afternoon, I **3** _____ English and then I go to book club. It **4** _____ at three o'clock. How do I get to the library from my class? I go **5** _____ and then I turn **6** _____ . School is fun!

1	o'clock	ten after	quarter to
2	quarter after	o'clock	time
3	has	have	am
4	starts	has	finish
5	turn left	turn right	straight
6	straight	turn left	right

Speaking

3 💬 **Look and tell the story.**

Jane's school day

3 Help at home

Learning Heroes

I want to learn new words for chores we do at home:

_____
_____
_____

Draw: a chore

I want to:
- 📖 a story
- 💬 about housework
- ▶ Onward video
- 🎧 about doing new things

Video quiz

1 Watch again. Read and number in order.

a) Ian is learning to drive. ☐
b) Ian is making breakfast. [1]
c) Barley is taking out the trash. ☐
d) Ian can drive, but he is worried. ☐
e) Blazey is eating the food on the floor. ☐
f) Ian is cleaning the floor. ☐

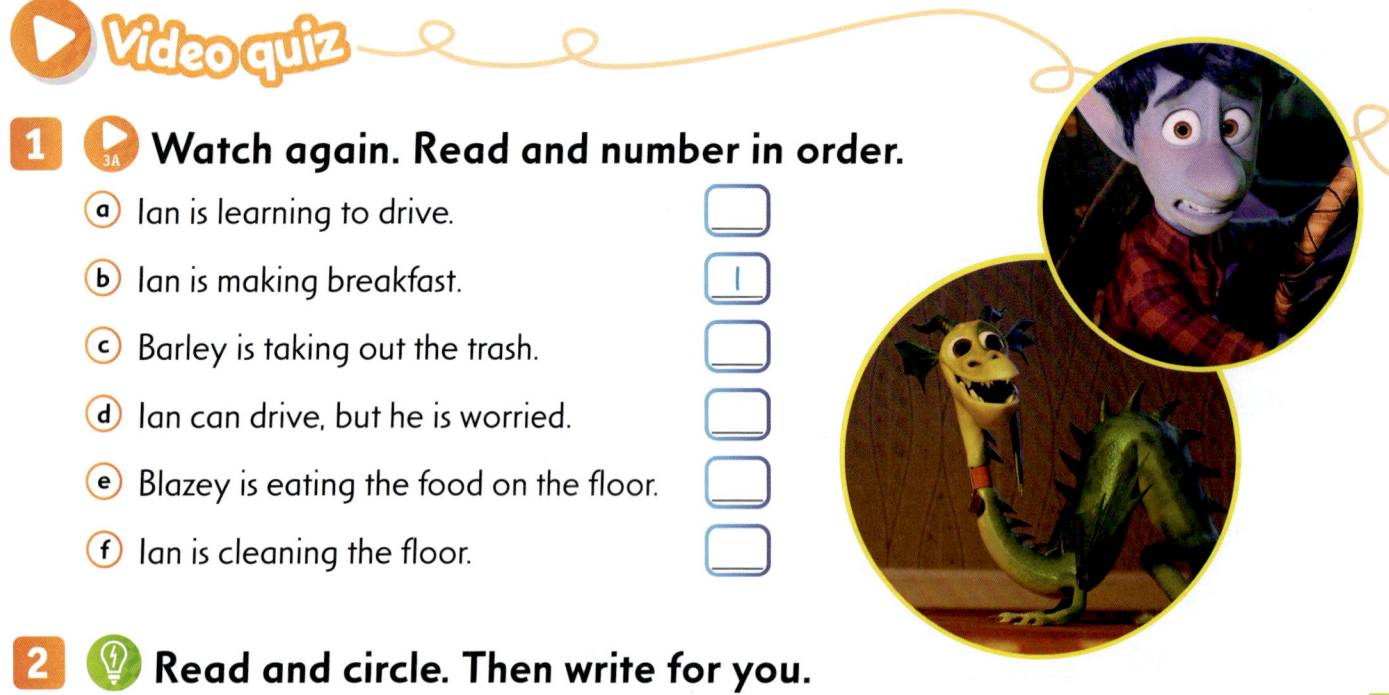

2 Read and circle. Then write for you.

1. Ian really **wants** / **doesn't want** to learn to drive.
2. He feels **happy** / **sad** when he can drive on the highway.
3. He feels **excited** / **nervous** when he can't drive on the highway.
4. What new thing do you really want to do? _____

LESSON 1 **Vocabulary**

3 Match. Then number the pictures.

1. make — breakfast
2. feed — my pet
3. take out — the trash
4. clean — the floor

Challenge!
Break the code. Then write.

9	1	14		1	14	4		2	1	18	12	5	25
				A									

4 Look, read, and write.

Every day I _____
and _____ .

I help at home. I _____
and _____ .

Extra time?
Write two things Ian does and one thing Barley does.

I can name chores at home.

29

LESSON 2
Vocabulary

1 Look and match. Check (✓) the missing activity.

1. cook a meal — f
2. clear the table
3. dry the dishes
4. make my bed
5. take care of my brother / sister
6. wash the dishes
7. set the table
8. water the plants

2 Read and write.

1. I need to clean up my bedroom.   I make my bed.
2. The garden is very dry.   _____
3. My little sister wants to go to the park.   _____
4. My parents can't make dinner every day.   _____
5. There are dishes on the table after lunch.   _____

Find out!
What other types of housework can robots do?

3 Write. How do you help at home?

I _____ in the morning.
I _____ after school.
I _____ in the evening.

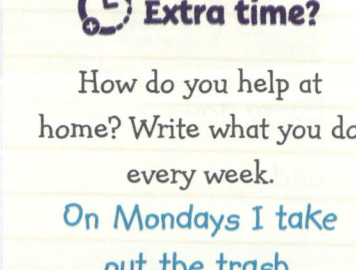

Extra time?
How do you help at home? Write what you do every week.
On Mondays I take out the trash.

I can name chores at home.

LESSON 3
Grammar

1 🎧 3.1 **Look, listen, and match.**

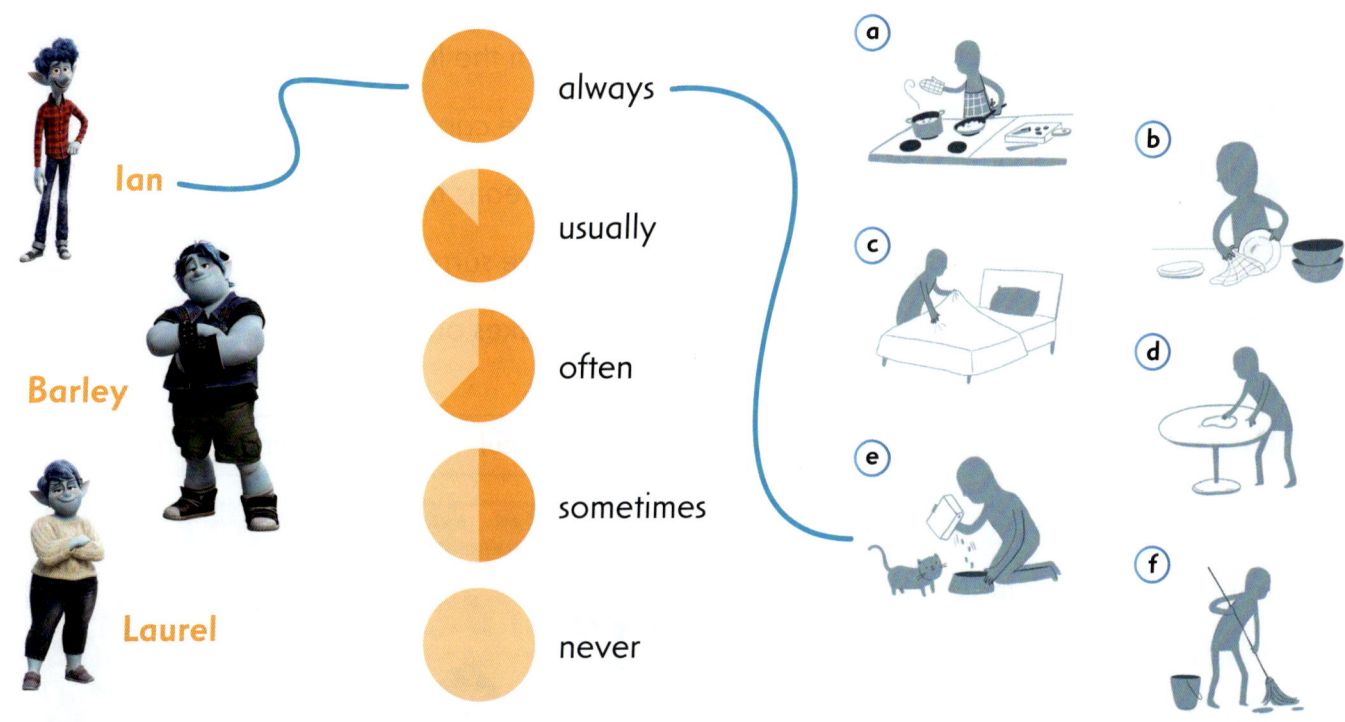

Grammar Heroes

🧩 **Read and think. Then write.**

How _____ does Ian have cereal for breakfast?

He _____ has cereal for breakfast.

How _____ do you make breakfast?

I _____ make breakfast.

2 Write about your family. Use *always*, *often*, *usually*, *sometimes*, and *never*.

1. My brother never takes out the trash.
2. _____
3. _____
4. _____
5. _____

Extra time?

Tell a friend about chores in your family.

I can talk about how often people do things.

A birthday surprise

**LESSON 4
Story**

1 **Remember the story. Read and match.**

1. Uma makes a list of things
2. Sato usually
3. Diego always
4. Uma does all the things
5. Uma's mom loves

a. on the list.
b. she can do for her mom.
c. cleans the floor.
d. the surprise.
e. takes out the trash.

2 **Read, choose, and write.**

<u>birthday</u>   beautiful   help   list   time   worried

It's Uma's mom's 1 ___birthday___ . Uma wants to make her mom happy. Uma makes a 2 _____ . She doesn't have 3 _____ to do all the things on the list. Her friends 4 _____ her. Uma wants to make a cake. She is 5 _____ . Her friends help her make the cake. The cake is 6 _____ .

Uma and her friends do all the things on the list. Uma's mom is happy!

3 **Read and write. Then compare with a friend.**

1. What new thing does Uma really want to do? <u>She wants to make a cake.</u>
2. How does she feel when she does it? _____
3. What new thing do you really want to do at home? _____
4. How do you feel about doing it? _____

I **like** / **don't like** the story because _____ .

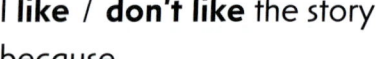 read a story about doing new things.

Extra time?

What do you think happens next in the story? Write and say.

LESSON 5
Vocabulary and Grammar

1 Look, read, and match.

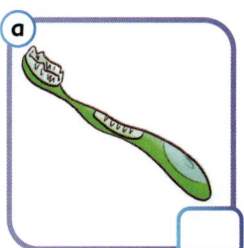

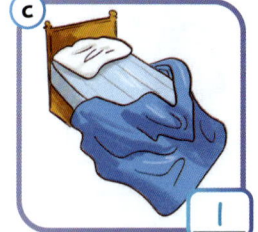
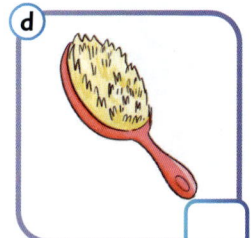
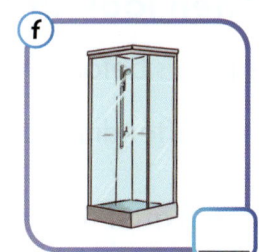

1. I get up.
2. I take a bath.
3. I brush my teeth.
4. I get dressed.
5. I take a shower.
6. I brush my hair.

2 🎧 3.2 Listen and check (✓). What do they do first?

3 Look at 2. Write questions with *before*.

1. What does he do before he brushes his teeth?

   He takes a bath.

2. _____

   She takes a shower.

3. _____

   He gets up.

⏰ Extra time?

What do you do in the morning, before you go to school? Write.

I can ask and answer questions about the order I do things.

33

LESSON 6
Listening and Speaking

1 🎧 3.3 **Listen and number in order.**

Our planner

2 🎧 3.4 **Read and write. Then look at 1 and match. Listen and check.**

1. She _____ the plants before she _____ the _____ .

   She _____ a bath after dinner. _____

2. He _____ his teeth after he gets up. Then he gets _____ .

   He _____ out the trash before he goes to school. _____

3 💬 **Ask a friend and draw. Then write about your friend.**

Morning

get up _____ _____ go to school

My friend _____ always _____ .

_____

What do you do after you get up?   I get dressed after I get up.

Extra time?
What do you do every day? Write.

I can use a planner to talk about daily routines.

Doing new things

LESSON 7
Myself and others
Self-management

1 🎧 Read and check (✓). What do you say to help your friends? Then listen and check.

1. I want to do more exercise. But I don't have time.
   - a) Exercise isn't interesting. ○
   - b) You can find 10 minutes a day to do it. ✓

2. I want to cook dinner. But I don't know how.
   - a) You can use a cook book. ○
   - b) Your brother can cook dinner. ○

3. I want to paint a picture. But I don't want people to laugh at me.
   - a) It doesn't matter what people think! ○
   - b) Don't paint a picture. ○

4. I want to learn how to play the guitar. But I don't know how.
   - a) You can use the internet. ○
   - b) Playing the guitar isn't fun. ○

5. I want to help at home more. But I don't know what to do.
   - a) Helping at home isn't interesting. ○
   - b) You can always ask how to help! ○

I can learn how to do new things.

2 💡 Read, think, and answer.

What hard thing do you really want to do? _____

What's stopping you? Check (✓).

- I don't know how to do it. ○
- I don't have time. ○
- I don't want people to laugh at me. ○

What's your plan? _____

My portfolio

3 💡 Make an *I can do it!* goal planner.

My goal planner

What do I want to do?
_____

What's stopping me?
_____

What's my plan?
1 _____
2 _____
3 _____

Be a hero!
Make a list of the new things to try this week.

Important inventions

LESSON 8 — My world

1 Correct the sentences.

1. We keep our food cold with GPS.
   We keep our food cold in fridges.

2. We make phone calls on our fridges.
   _____

3. Electricity helps us find our way on journeys.
   _____

4. Cell phones make our computers work.
   _____

2 Write. Then add more examples.

keep fruit fresh   ~~send a message~~   ~~use a tablet~~   talk to my parents   watch TV   find a police station   keep ice cream cold

electricity	fridge	cell phone	GPS
use a tablet	_____	_send a message_	_____
_____	_____	_____	_____
_____	_____	_____	_____

3 Look, choose, and write.

cell phone   Electricity   TV

How does it work?

You talk into your _____ : "Turn on the _____ !" It sends a message to your house. _____ goes to the TV. The TV turns on.

Extra time?

What other things can you do on your cell phone? Write a list.
turn off the TV
play music

I can read and talk about inventions.

A class survey

LESSON 9
Project

1 Complete the web diagram. Follow the steps.

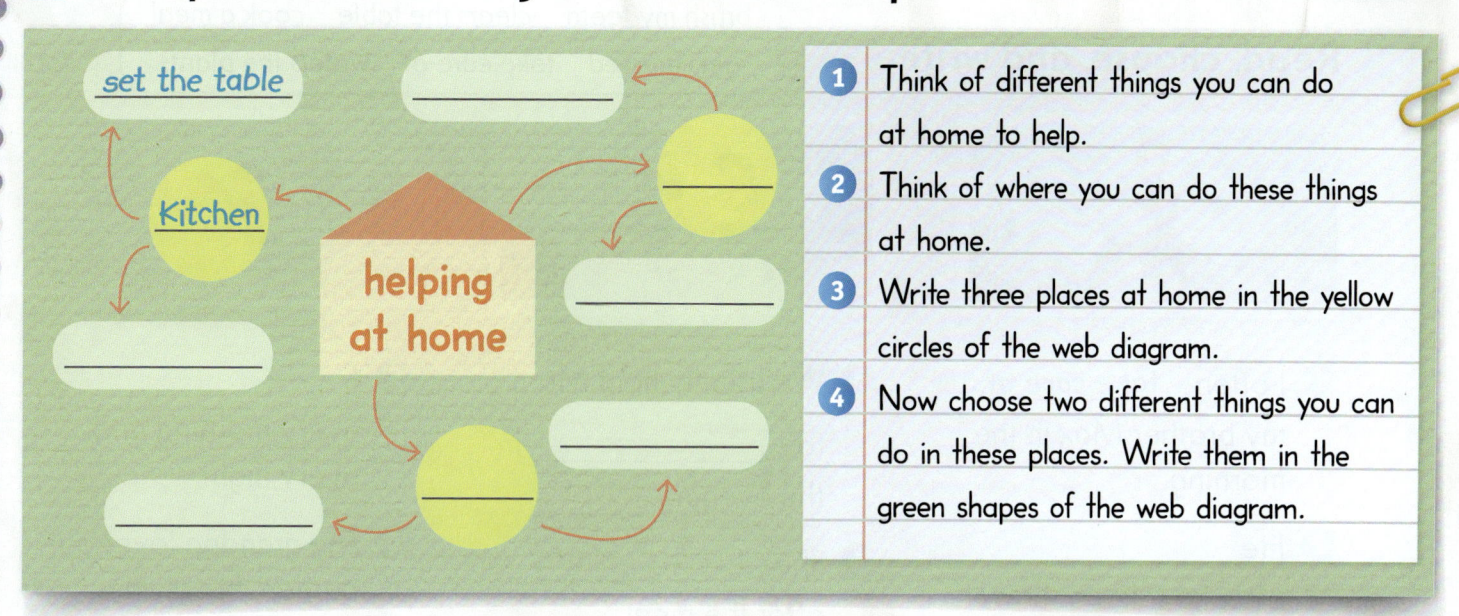

set the table

Kitchen

helping at home

1. Think of different things you can do at home to help.
2. Think of where you can do these things at home.
3. Write three places at home in the yellow circles of the web diagram.
4. Now choose two different things you can do in these places. Write them in the green shapes of the web diagram.

2 Think of questions and complete. Then ask and answer.

How often do you ...	always	_____	often	sometimes	_____
set the table?	✔				
_____					
_____					
_____					

Check!

There are questions that start with. 'How often ...? ○

There are question marks (?) after each question. ○

3 Reflect on your project.

My web diagram is clear and simple.
☆☆☆☆☆

My web diagram helps organize my ideas.
☆☆☆☆☆

My class survey

Do you have six questions? _____

Which chores do you ask about in your survey?
_____

Which chores do children do at home most often? _____

I can use a web diagram to create a survey about helping at home.

My progress journal

**LESSON 10
Review**

| brush my teeth | clears the table | cook a meal |
| gets dressed | ~~take care of~~ | waters the plants |

1 Read, choose, and write.

1. I often take care of my brother Max in the morning.
2. He _____ after he takes a shower.
3. We usually help Mom to _____ in the evening.
4. She _____ after the meal.
5. I _____ every morning and every night.
6. My grandpa loves our garden. He always _____ .

2 Complete. Then ask and answer with a friend.

How often do you wash the dishes? — I sometimes wash the dishes.

1. How _____ do you _____ ? — I usually _____ .
2. How _____ do you _____ ? — _____
3. _____ — _____

3 What I know.

Write. What's your school morning routine? _____

Say. Talk about this scene from the video. What happens? Do you like it?

Star progress

- This unit was ☆☆☆☆☆
- My favorite lesson is _____ because _____ .
- I can now _____ .

UNIT 3
Exam practice

Listening

1 🎧 3.6 **Listen and match.**

Charlie
Sally — c
Sam and Fred
Mr. Smith
Mrs. Smith

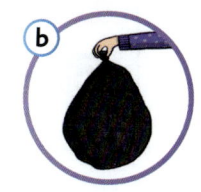

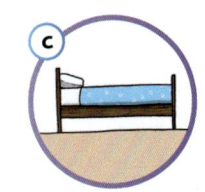

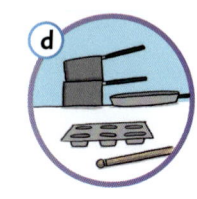

a   b   c   d   e

Reading and Writing

2 **Look, read, and write.**

Complete the sentences.

1. The girl's dress is _____red_____ .
2. The boy is reading a book about _____ .
3. The father is _____ .

Answer the questions.

4. What's the girl in the red dress doing?
   _____
5. What's the boy in a white T-shirt doing? _____

Write a sentence about the picture.

6. _____

Speaking

3 💬 **Answer the questions for you.**

What do you do before school?

What do you usually do in the afternoons?

How often do you help your family?

What do you do to help your family?

39

4 Our hobbies

Learning Heroes

I want to learn hobby words:
☐ _____
☐ _____
☐ _____

Draw: a hobby

I want to:
- 📖 a story
- 💬 about hobbies ○
- ▶ Coco video ○
- 🎧 about following a dream ○

Video quiz

1 **Watch again. Read and match.**

1. Miguel looks at photographs with
2. Miguel's favorite hobby is
3. Miguel is learning to
4. Miguel's family makes
5. Miguel's great great grandfather was
6. Miguel's grandmother is angry because

a. a famous musician.
b. beautiful shoes.
c. his grandmother.
d. Miguel wants to be a musician.
e. playing music.
f. play the guitar.

2 **Read and answer. Then write for you.**

1. What's Miguel's dream? _____
2. Is Miguel's family happy about his dream? _____
3. What's your dream? _____
4. Does your family like your dream? Why? _____

40

LESSON 1 Vocabulary

3 Look, choose, and write.

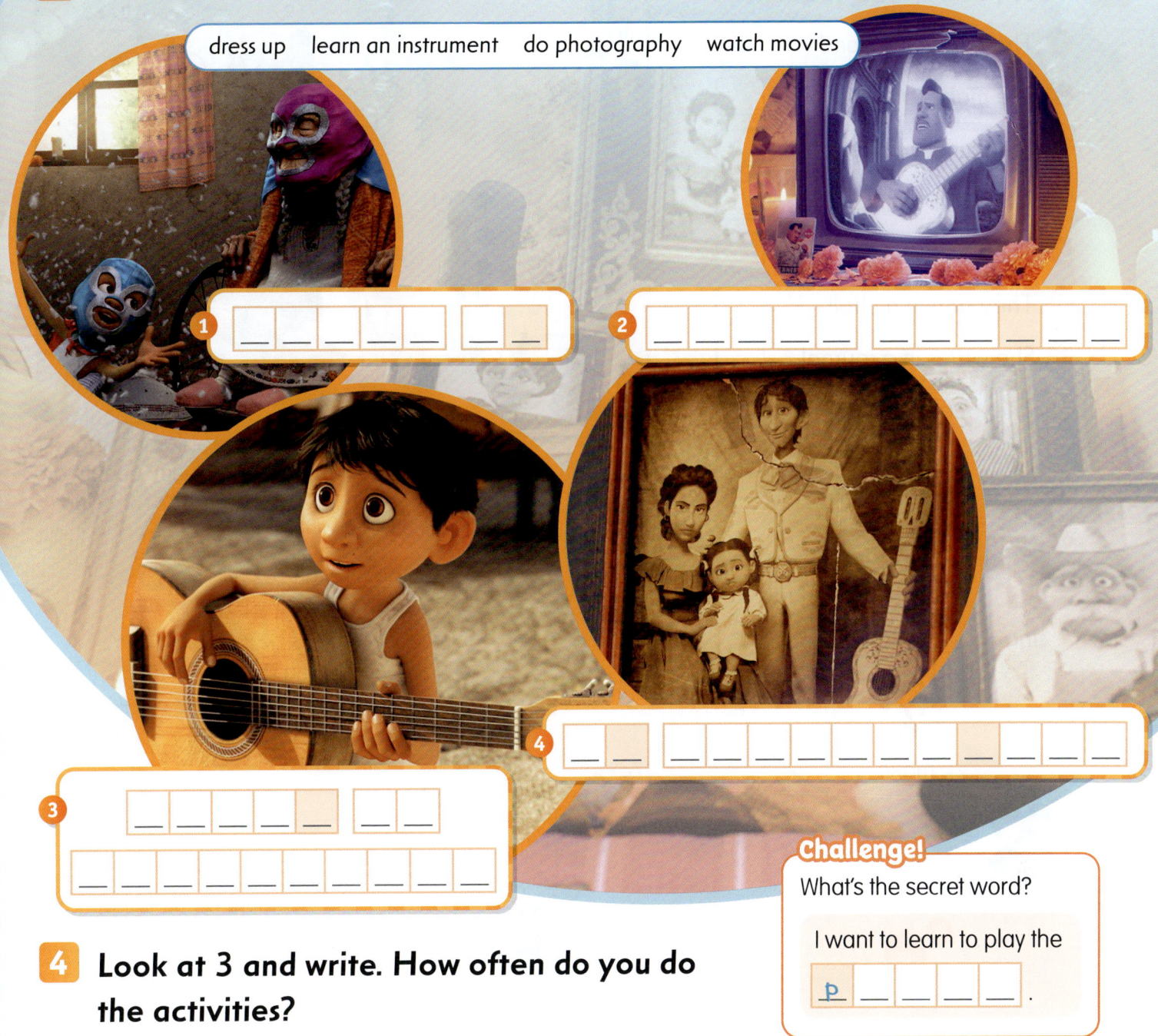

dress up   learn an instrument   do photography   watch movies

1. _ _ _ _ _ _ _
2. _ _ _ _ _ _ _ _ _ _
3. _ _ _ _ _ _ _ / _ _ _ _ _ _ _ _ _ _
4. _ _ _ _ _ _ _ _ _ _ _ _

Challenge!
What's the secret word?

I want to learn to play the
p _ _ _ _ _ .

4 Look at 3 and write. How often do you do the activities?

never   often   sometimes   usually

1. I _____ dress up.
2. I _____ .
3. _____
4. _____

Extra time?
Ask a friend. How often do they do the activities in 3?

I can name hobbies.

41

LESSON 2
Vocabulary

1 **Look, read, and match.**

1. They play in a band. — *b*
2. She makes models.
3. He paints pictures.
4. She reads comics.
5. They go cycling.
6. They sing in a choir.
7. She writes in a journal.
8. They make movies.

2 **Follow and write.**

1. sing
2. make
3. paint
4. go
5. play
6. read

a. They *paint pictures*.

b. She _____.

c. They _____.

d. _____

e. _____

f. _____

Find out!
Find out about a world-famous band. How many people are in the band? What do they play?

Extra time?
Write about your hobbies and a friend's hobbies.

I can name hobbies.

LESSON 3
Grammar

1 🎧 4.1 **Listen and circle T (True) or F (False). Correct the false sentences.**

1. Miguel's family likes doing photography. **T** / F
2. Miguel doesn't like dressing up. T / F
3. Miguel doesn't like playing the guitar. T / F
4. Miguel and his dog like watching movies. T / F
5. Miguel's family likes making shoes. T / F
6. Miguel likes making shoes. T / F

Grammar Heroes

🧩 **Read and write.**

Does Miguel _____ making shoes?   No, he _____ .

Does Miguel _____ _____ the guitar?   Yes, he _____ .

2 **Complete the chart for you. Then write.**

	Paula	Me
watching movies	🙂	🙂
reading comics	☹	🙂
singing in a choir	🙂	🙂
doing photography	☹	🙂

Paula likes 1 ___watching movies___ .
She doesn't like 2 ___reading comics___ .
She 3 _____ .
She 4 _____ .

I like 5 _____ .
I don't like 6 _____ .
7 _____
8 _____

⏰ **Extra time?**
Look at 2. Ask and answer.

I can talk about hobbies I like and don't like doing.

43

Sato's dream

LESSON 4 Story

1 Remember the story. Number in order.

a. Sato goes to Uma's mom's movie studio.
b. The children make a movie.
c. Sato's dream is to make movies. `1`
d. Lucy shows Sato how to make movies with a phone.
e. The children watch the movie.
f. The children tell her to follow her dream.

2 Read, choose, and write.

~~Max~~   Uma   Diego   Sato   Lucy   the children

1. I like going cycling. _____Max_____
2. I like watching movies. _____
3. You have to keep trying! _____
4. Sometimes I make movies with my phone. _____
5. I like making movies! _____
6. We like watching movies! _____

3 Read and write. Then compare with a friend.

1 Sato's journal

Sato's dream is __to make movies__.
But she doesn't know how to _____.
She can visit _____.
She can make a movie with _____.

2 My journal

My dream is _____.
But I don't know how to _____.
I can _____.
I can _____.

Storytellers club

My favorite character is _____
because _____.

Extra time?

Imagine a different ending to the story. Write and draw.

I can read a story about following dreams.

44

LESSON 5
Vocabulary and Grammar

1 🎧 **Listen and circle.**

1. exciting / (cool)
2. boring / hard
3. cool / easy
4. terrible / hard
5. boring / exciting
6. easy / terrible

2 Look, read, and write.

a. 
1 __What do__ you like
2 __doing__ in your free time?
I like 3 __going cycling__.
Why?
4 __Because__ it's easy.

b. 
1 _____ Mark like
2 _____ in his free time?
He likes 3 _____.
4 _____?
5 _____ it's cool.

3 💬 **Answer for you. Then ask a friend and write.**

What do you like doing in your free time? Why?
I _____ because _____ .
What about your friend?
_____ likes _____ because _____ .

Extra time?
Write a list of all the opposites you know.
tall – short

I can talk about why I like doing activities.

45

LESSON 6
Listening and Speaking

1 🎧 **Listen and write.**

1. 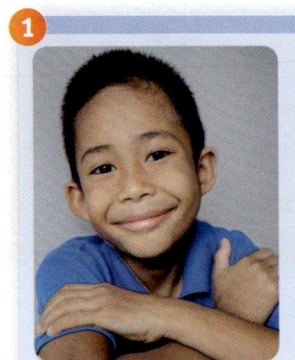
Name: Tony
Activity: _____
Likes: Yes / No
Why: ____exciting____
Day: _____

2. 
Name: Ellen
Activity: _____
Likes: Yes / No
Why: _____
Day: _____

2 Look, write, and circle.

Kim's activities	Saturday		Sunday	
Morning	1 guitar 🙂	2 camera ☹	3 comic ☹	4 laptop ☹

1. Kim ____likes____ learning an _____ because it's **easy** / **boring**.
2. She _____ doing _____ because it's **hard** / **cool**.
3. Kim _____ reading _____ because it's **exciting** / **boring**.
4. She _____ _____ doing _____ because it's **easy** / **hard**.

3 💬 **Complete your activities program and write. Ask and answer.**

1. I like _____ because _____.

2. I _____ because _____.

	Saturday	Sunday
Morning		
Afternoon		

Why do you like … ?

Extra time?
Ask your family. What do they like doing in their free time?

46 **I can** use an activity program to talk about what I like doing.

LESSON 7
Myself and others
Self-awareness

Following your dream

1 Read and match.

1. I love movies. I want to be an actor.
2. I want to help people. My dream is to become a doctor.
3. I love soccer. My dream is to become a soccer player.
4. I want to help animals. I want to be a vet.
5. I like designing houses. I want to be an architect.

a. I can go to art club and learn to draw.
b. I can act in drama class at school.
c. I can get a pet and learn to take care of it.
d. I can play on the school soccer team.
e. I can study medicine at college.

2 Read, think, and write.

1. What do you love doing?
   _____

2. What's your dream?
   _____

3. How can you follow your dream?
   I can _____ .
   I can _____ .
   I can _____ .

My portfolio

3 Create your own vision board.

Following my dreams!

My dream is _____ .

I can _____ .

Then I can _____ .

Then I can _____ .

Be a hero!
Share your vision board with a friend. Say something nice!

I can talk about following my dreams.

47

Musical instruments

LESSON 8 — My world

1 Read and write.

1. What family is the guitar in? — _string_
2. How many strings do most guitars have? _____
3. What parts of the body do we use to play the flute? _____
4. What brass instrument is in the text? _____

2 Look and circle the odd one out. Then write why.

1. a wind instrument
2. _____
3. _____
4. _____

3 Look, read, and circle. Then think and write.

The serpent

It's a **1** wind / string instrument.

You play it with your **2** feet and mouth / fingers and mouth. It's a **3** loud / quiet instrument. It **4** can / can't make different sounds. It looks like a snake.

My instrument

What is it? _____

_____

I can read and talk about musical instruments.

Extra time?

Draw and label your new instrument. Describe it to a friend.

A movie storyboard

**LESSON 9
Project**

1 💬 **Complete for you and your two friends.**

What do you like doing? Why?

Name			
What do they like doing?			
Why?			

🎬 **Movie storyboard: my friends' hobbies**

_____ likes _____ because it's _____ .

_____ likes _____ _____ .

_____ likes _____ _____ .

2 🎧 **Read, listen, and circle. Then practice your presentation with a friend.**

1. When we give a presentation we speak **loudly** / **quietly**.
2. When we give a presentation we speak **quickly** / **slowly**.

Check!
There are sentences about what happens in the movie. ⭕
I use *because* to explain the pictures. ⭕

3 Reflect on your project.

I explained the pictures in my storyboard:
☆☆☆☆☆

I look at my friends when I talk:
☆☆☆☆☆

My movie storyboard
Do you write why your friends like their hobbies? _____
Do you have pictures of their hobbies? _____
Do you explain the pictures? _____

I can make and present a movie storyboard about hobbies.

49

LESSON 10
Review

My progress journal

1 **Look, read, and circle.**
1. Diego **watches movies** / **goes cycling** on the weekend.
2. Uma likes **reading comics** / **playing in a band**.
3. Zoe **writes in a journal** / **sings in a choir** in the park.
4. Sato likes **learning an instrument** / **dressing up**.
5. Max likes painting pictures because it's **cool** / **terrible**.
6. He doesn't like making models because it's **easy** / **hard**.

2 **Write. Then ask and answer with a friend.**
1. _____Do_____ you _____like_____ watching movies?
2. _____ you like _____ in a choir?
3. _____ do you like _____ in your free time?

3 **What I know.**

Write. What's your favorite free time activity?
_____

Say. Talk about this scene from the video.
What happens? Do you like it?

Star progress
- This unit was ☆☆☆☆☆
- My favorite lesson is _____
  because _____ .
- I can now _____

50

UNIT 4
Exam practice

Listening

1 🎧 **Listen and write.**

🏃 The Activity Center

1. Name of the center: ____Playday____ Center
2. Grace likes: _____
3. She doesn't like: _____
4. The center opens at: _____
5. Grace wants to _____ on Saturday morning.
6. She can help her mom _____ on Saturday afternoon.

Reading and Writing

2 **Read, choose, and write.**

go cycling   dress up   music

guitar   band   plant

1. This is a musical instrument. ____guitar____
2. We listen and dance to this. _____
3. When we do this, we put on clothes and have fun. _____
4. This is a group of people who play music together. _____
5. When you ride a bike you do this. _____

Speaking

3 💬 **Look and say. What is different?**

5 Let's cook!

Learning Heroes

I want to learn new food words:
_____
_____
_____

Draw: a recipe I want to cook

I want to:
- 📖 a story
- 💬 about food
- ▶️ Ratatouille video
- 🎧 about fixing problems

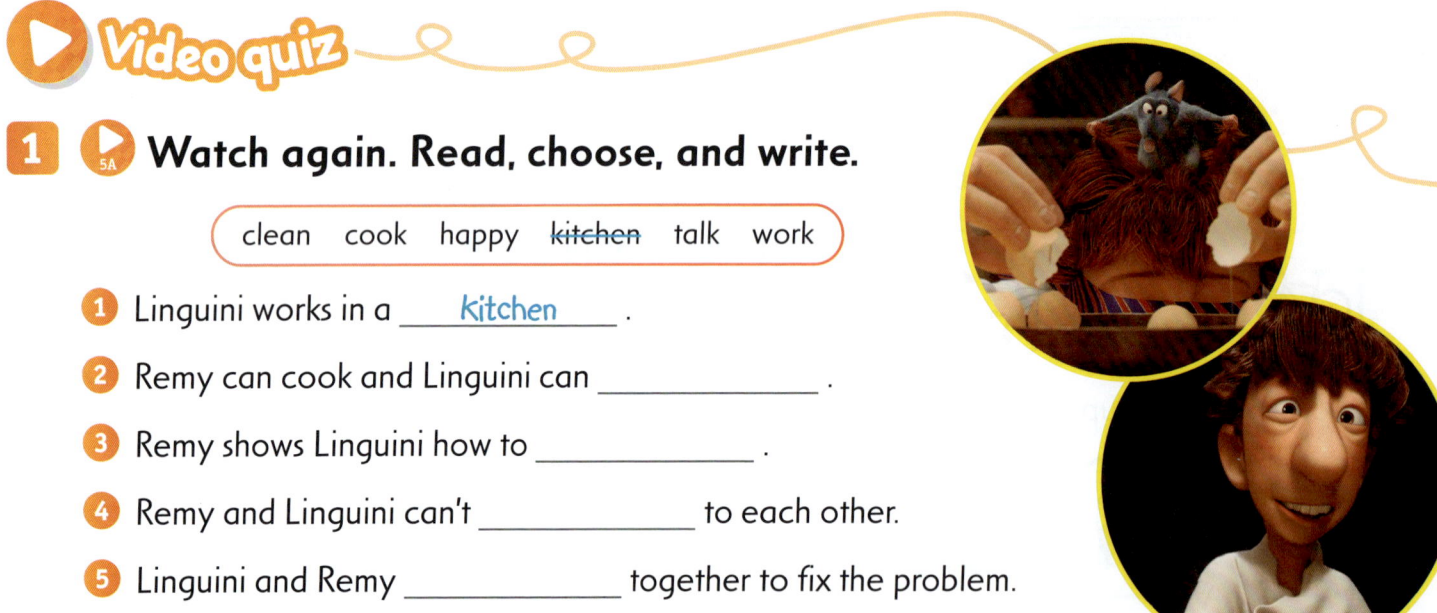

Video quiz

1 Watch again. Read, choose, and write.

clean   cook   happy   ~~kitchen~~   talk   work

1. Linguini works in a __kitchen__ .
2. Remy can cook and Linguini can _____ .
3. Remy shows Linguini how to _____ .
4. Remy and Linguini can't _____ to each other.
5. Linguini and Remy _____ together to fix the problem.
6. Linguini and Remy are _____ .

2 Read, choose, and complete. Then write for you.

Remy   Linguini   Remy and Linguini

1. _____ has a problem. He can't cook.
2. _____ helps him to fix the problem. He teaches him to cook.
3. _____ feel happy after they fix the problem.
4. What problem do you want to fix this week? Who can you work with? _____

52

LESSON 1 Vocabulary

3 Write the missing words.

1. pan
2. _____
3. _____
4. _____

4 Read, choose, and write.

> bowl   cup   pan   ~~plate~~

Remi and Linguini cook dinner. They put bread on a
1 ____plate____ and soup in a 2 _____ .
There is juice in the 3 _____ and meat in the
4 _____ . Dinner is delicious!

Challenge!
Circle. Write the missing word.

a	c	u	p	a	b
p	p	l	a	t	e
w	o	u	n	r	a

_____

Extra time?
Draw and write three things you can find in your kitchen.

I can name things in the kitchen.

53

LESSON 2
Vocabulary

1 Look, choose, and write.

> hot chocolate   milkshake   pancakes   ~~ratatouille~~   salad   strawberries   vegetables   water

1. It's a plate of _ratatouille_.
2. It's a pan of _____.
3. It's a bowl of green _____.
4. It's a plate of _____ and ice cream.
5. It's a bowl of _____.
6. It's a glass of _____.
7. It's a banana _____.
8. It's a cup of _____.

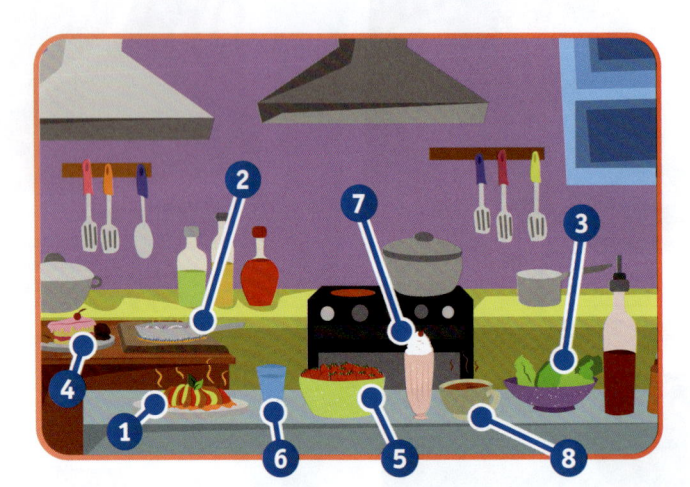

2 Read and write. Use phrases from 1.

1. What would you like?
   I'm very thirsty. _I'd like a glass of water_.
   Do you like vegetables and French food?
   Yes, I do. _____.

2. Would you like to eat something?
   Yes, something cold. _____.
   Are you thirsty?
   Yes, but I don't want water or juice. _____.

3. Would you like some pancakes?
   No, thanks. I want some fruit. _____.
   Would you like to drink something hot?
   Yes. _____.

Find out! Find two other traditional foods from France.

Extra time? What did you have for breakfast today? Write or say.

I can name food and drinks.

54

LESSON 3
Grammar

1 Look, read, and circle.
1. (There's) / There isn't a bowl of salad.
2. There are some / There aren't any pancakes.
3. There's some / There isn't any hot chocolate.
4. There are two / There aren't any milkshakes.
5. There is / There isn't a pan of ratatouille.
6. There are some / There aren't any vegetables.

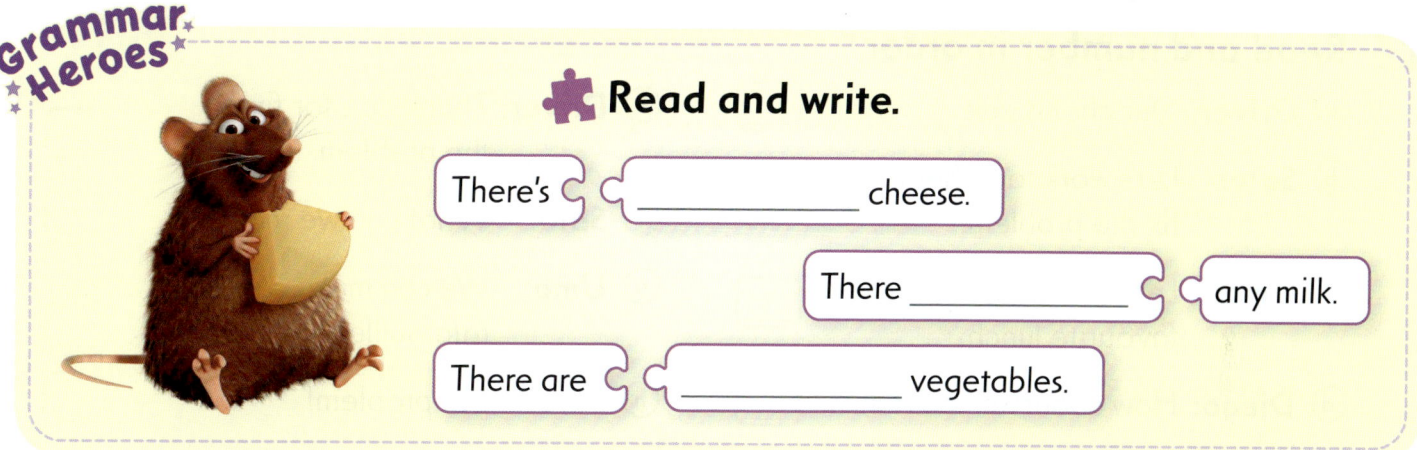

Grammar Heroes

Read and write.

There's — _____ cheese.

There _____ — any milk.

There are — _____ vegetables.

2 Look and write. What's in the kitchen?
1. There are four plates of _____ vegetables.
2. There isn't any _____ salad.
3. _____ of ratatouille.
4. _____ pancakes.
5. _____ water.
6. _____
7. _____
8. _____

Extra time?
Think about your fridge at home. What's in it? Write a list.

I can use *there is / are* with countable and uncountable nouns.

What's for lunch?

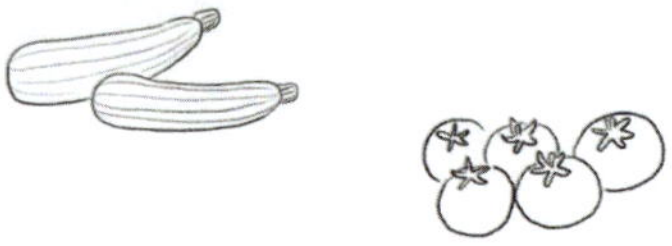

LESSON 4
Story

1 Remember the story. Read and match.

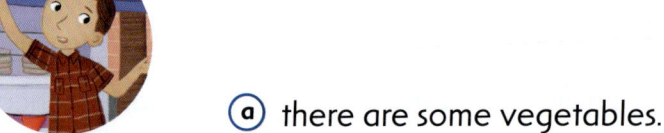

1. There isn't any lunch
2. The children work together
3. They can make ratatouille
4. The driver is happy

because

a. there are some vegetables.
b. the children fix the problem.
c. the chef is sick.
d. they want to fix the problem.

2 Read and number in order.

a. **Driver:** Our chef is sick.
b. **Sato:** Let's work together to fix the problem.
c. **Uma:** Let's go and get our favourite lunch. `1`
d. **Diego:** How about we cook lunch?
e. **Driver:** Thank you for fixing the problem, kids.
f. **Sato:** What can we make?
g. **Uma:** We can make ratatouille!
h. **Sato:** No problem!

3 Read and write. Then compare with a friend.

1. The man in the story has a problem. There isn't any lunch because the chef is sick.

   What do the children say? _____
   What do the children do? _____

2. Imagine there isn't any lunch at school today because the chef is sick.

   What do you say? _____
   What do you do? _____

Storytellers club

I think the story is _____
because _____.

I can read a story about fixing a problem.

Extra time?
Write a different ending for the story.

56

LESSON 5
Vocabulary and Grammar

1 Look, circle, and write.

(zucchinis)saucesaltgarlicpeppereggplants

1. There are a lot of ___zucchinis___ .
2. There are a few _____ .
3. There's some _____ .
4. There's a lot of _____ .
5. There's a little _____ .
6. There isn't any _____ .

2 🎧 5.1 Listen, and put a ✔ or ✘.

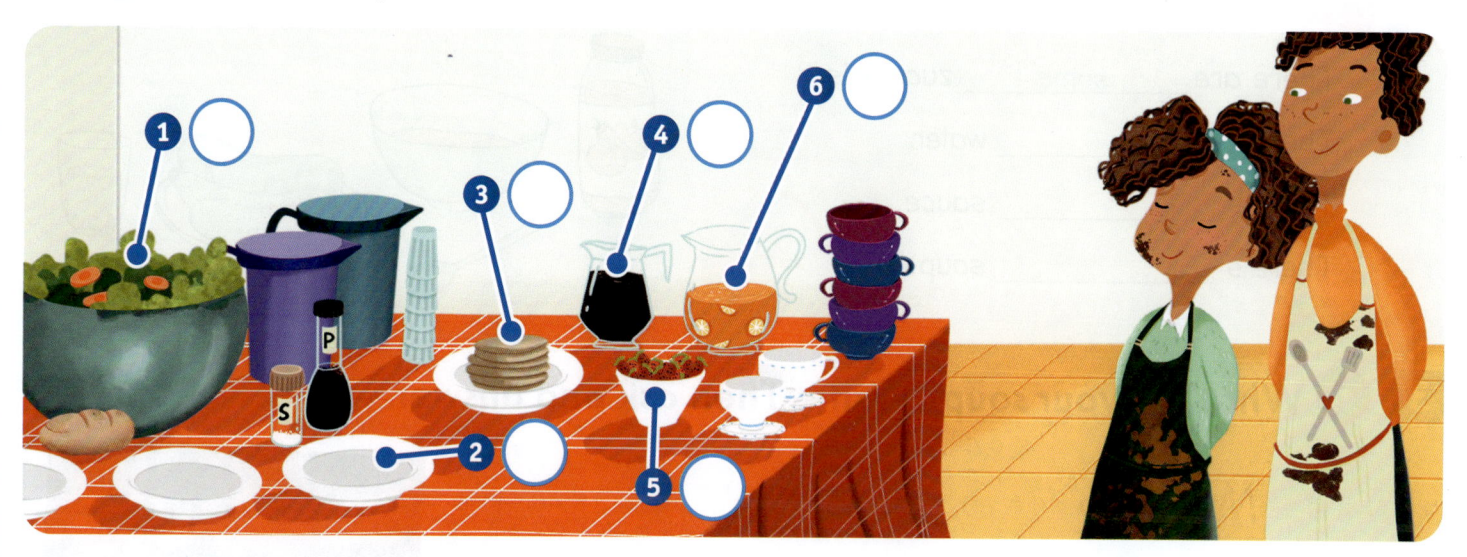

3 Look at 2. Read and complete.

1. ___How much___ pepper is there? ___There's some___ pepper.
2. _____ bowls _____ ? _____ bowls.
3. _____ bread _____ ? _____ bread.
4. _____ _____
5. _____ _____

Extra time?

Look in your classroom. Write three things we can't count.

I can ask and answer questions with *how much* and *how many*.

57

LESSON 6
Listening and Speaking

1 🎧 5.2 **Listen and check (✓).**

1. a ✓ b
2. a b
3. a b
4. a b

2 **Look and write. What's in the soup?** ~~some~~   a lot of   some   a little

Zucchini and tomato soup

There are ____some____ zucchinis.
There's _____ water.
There's _____ sauce.
There's _____ soup.

3 💬 **What's in your soup? Write. Then ask and answer.**

My soup
There's a little pepper.
_____
_____
_____
_____

Is there any pepper in your soup?

Yes, there is. There's a little pepper.

⏰ **Extra time?**
Think of your kitchen.
Make a shopping list.

58   **I can** ask and answer questions with *how much* and *how many*.

LESSON 7
Myself and others
Responsible decision-making

Fixing problems

1 Look and think. What are Emma's problems?

Sunday Picnic Lunch:

Food / Drink
café: closed
bakery: closed
supermarket: open

Where / When Green Park, 1 p.m.

Likes / Dislikes
Jim, Jenny, Sam, Lou don't like tomatoes.
Dan, Rina, Sally, Frank don't like onions.
Rina and Sally don't like cookies.
Everyone loves fruit, sandwiches, and cheese.

Dan, Frank, and Lou can't come until 1:30.

2 How can you help Emma? Share ideas with a friend.

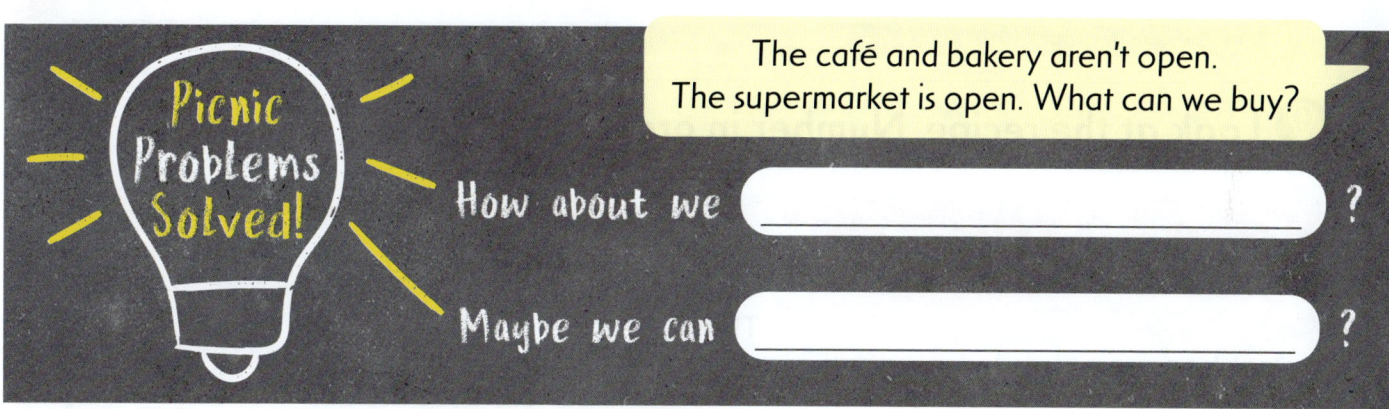

Picnic Problems Solved!

The café and bakery aren't open. The supermarket is open. What can we buy?

How about we _____?

Maybe we can _____?

My portfolio

3 What's for lunch at the picnic? Write and draw. Then read and check (✔).

My solution
_____
_____
_____

Can you fix problems?

I can share ideas about fixing a problem. ○

I can listen to my friends' ideas about fixing a problem. ○

I can fix a food problem with my friends. ○

Be a hero!
Share a problem with a friend. How do you solve it? Discuss.

I can fix problems.

59

Food technology

Following a recipe

**LESSON 8
My world**

1 Look, choose, and write.   cut   fry   ~~peel~~   stir

Vegetable Stir-fry

- First, ____peel____ the vegetables.
- Then _____ the zucchini, eggplant, and tomatoes.
- Next, _____ the onions.
- Finally, _____ the vegetables.
- Eat with bread.

2 Look at the recipe. Number in order. Then write.

Fried Bananas

Peel bananas. [1]
Fry. [ ]
Stir. [ ]
Cut bananas. [ ]

- First, ____peel the bananas____ .
- Then _____ .
- Next, _____ in a pan.
- Finally, _____ slowly. Add some honey and salt.
- Eat with ice cream.

3 Invent a new recipe. What's in it? Write.

Name: _____
First, _____ .
Then _____ .
Next, _____ .
Finally, _____ .

I can read and write a recipe.

Extra time?
Find a soup recipe you like. Why do you like it?

A recipe

**LESSON 9
Project**

1 🎧 5.3 Listen and check (✓). Which group is working together?

Group 1 ⚪   Group 2 ⚪

2 Think about your recipe. What ingredients does it have? Check (✓) and write.

- strawberries ⚪
- vegetables ⚪
- water ⚪
- zucchini ⚪
- sauce ⚪
- salt ⚪

Ingredients
_____ _____ _____
_____ _____

Circle the words to show the steps. Can you write one more?

bowl   cup   cut   pan
peel   plate   stir
_____

Method

1   2   3   4

First, _____ .   Next, _____ .
Then _____ .   Finally, _____ .

Can you add anything else?
Eat with _____ .

Check!
Do you have three or four steps in your recipe? ⚪
Are your sentences short and simple? ⚪

3 Reflect on your project.

We gave each friend a different job:
☆☆☆☆☆

I make decisions that most of my friends agree with:
☆☆☆☆☆

My recipe
Are there pictures to show what to do? _____
Do you like your recipe? Why? _____

I can work in a group to create a recipe.

**LESSON 10
Review**

My progress journal

1 Read, choose, and write.

bowl   ~~cup~~   pancakes   salad   sauce   water

This is my kitchen. There's a 1 __cup__ of hot chocolate for me and soup in a 2 _____ for my mom. Can you see the 3 _____ in the pan? They're for Uma and Max. We're having dinner together. There's tomato 4 _____, pasta, and a plate of 5 _____, too. I always have a glass of 6 _____ with dinner.

2 Read and circle.

1. There are **any** / **(some)** pans in the kitchen.
2. **There's** / **There are** two plates of strawberries.
3. There are a **few** / **little** eggplants.
4. How **much** / **many** garlic is there? There's a little.

3 What I know.

Write. What's there in your fridge?

_____

Say. Talk about this scene from the video.
What happens? Do you like it?

Star progress

- This unit was ☆☆☆☆☆
- My favorite lesson is _____
  because _____.
- I can now _____.

UNIT 5
Exam practice

Listening

1 🎧 5.4 **Listen and match.**

Julia — Matt

Daisy — Vicky

Mike — Ben

Reading and Writing

2 **Look at 1. Read and write.**

The picnic

The children are on a picnic. They are eating and drinking. Vicky loves picnics!

"How many sandwiches are there?" asks Vicky.

"There are some sandwiches," says Daisy, "take one more."

"I don't like picnics. It's hot and I want to drink water," says Matt. Matt drinks a lot of water. "Do you want a milkshake, too?" asks Julia. "There's a little milkshake."

"No, thank you. I'm fine," says Matt.

1. Vicky loves ___picnics___ .
2. There are _____ sandwiches.
3. Matt is hot and he drinks _____ water.
4. There is _____ milkshake.
5. Matt doesn't want the _____ .

Speaking

3 💬 **Look at the pictures in 1 and in 3. Tell the story.**

The picnic

6 Going places

Learning Heroes

I want to learn new words about places in a city:

_____
_____
_____

Draw: a place in a city

I want to:
- 📖 a story ○
- 💬 about places in a city ○
- ▶ Bolt video ○
- 🎧 about learning new things ○

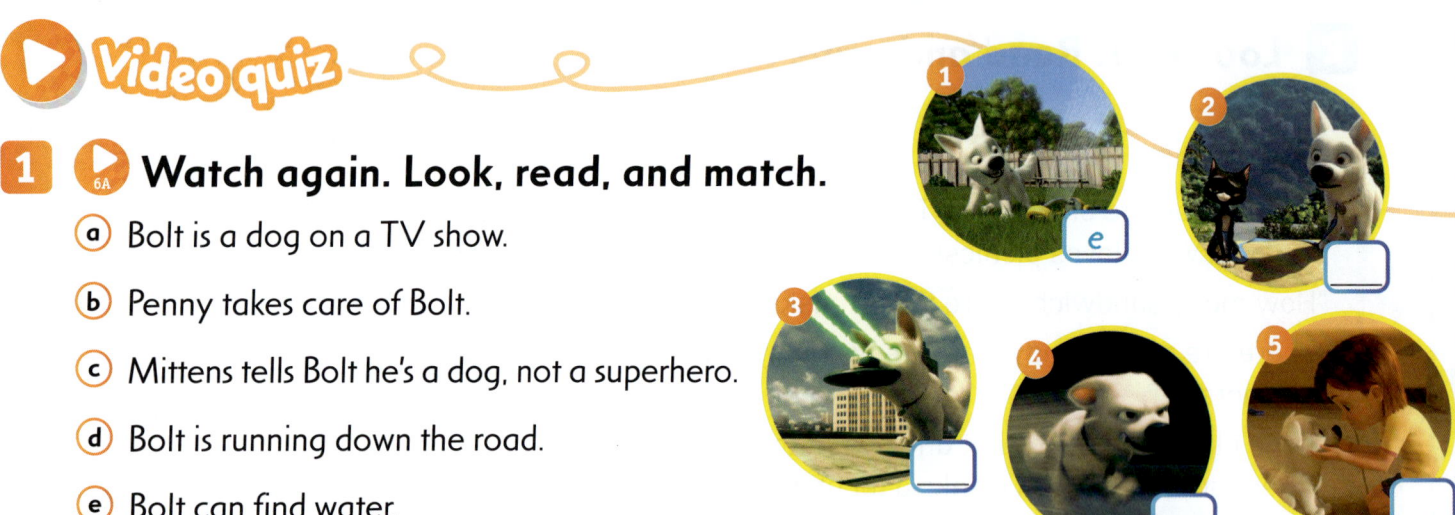

Video quiz

1 **Watch again. Look, read, and match.** (6A)

a) Bolt is a dog on a TV show.
b) Penny takes care of Bolt.
c) Mittens tells Bolt he's a dog, not a superhero.
d) Bolt is running down the road.
e) Bolt can find water.

1 — e

2 **Read and check (✓). Then write for you.**

① What does Bolt learn to do?

- ask for food ○
- put his head out of the door ○
- get the stick ○
- play with other dogs ○
- find milk ○

② What new thing do you want to learn? _____

③ Is it easy or hard? _____

LESSON 1 Vocabulary

3 Look, choose, and write. Then help Bolt find Penny.

building   road
sidewalk   signpost

challenge!

1 _____
2 _____
3 _____
4 _____

4 Look, read, and write. Then tell a friend about where you live.

My apartment block is in a city. It's on a long **1** ___road___ . The **2** _____ outside my apartment has trees. There's a **3** _____ for the train station. The **4** _____ next to my block is a bookstore.

Extra time?

Draw three new words from the lesson. Ask a friend to guess what they are.

I can name things in the city.

LESSON 2
Vocabulary

1 Look, write, and match.

> airport   ~~bus station~~   circus   gas station   market   movie studio   RV park   subway station

1. There are red buses at the ___bus station___ . **b**
2. The _____ is under the bus station. ☐
3. There are two planes at the _____ . ☐
4. There's a _____ next to the river. ☐
5. They're making movies at the _____ . ☐
6. People are having a picnic at the _____ . ☐

2 Look at 1. Read and write. Where are they?

1. Jenny and Paolo aren't working this week.
   They're at the RV park.
2. Pat is underground.
   She's _____ .
3. Carl is driving, but he isn't driving a car.
   _____
4. Anna and Mia are waiting to fly.
   _____

Find out!
How many people use the subway in New York city every year?

Extra time?
What places does your town or city have?

I can name places in a city.

LESSON 3
Grammar

1 🎧 6.1 **Look, read, and circle. Then listen and check.**

1
Where's Bolt **go** / **going**?
He's / **They're** going home.

2
Is / **Am** Penny going to the bus station?
No / **Yes**, she isn't.

3
Where **is** / **are** Bolt and Penny going?
They **are** / **aren't** going to the movie studio.

4
Are **they** / **she** going to the circus?
No / **Yes**, they aren't.

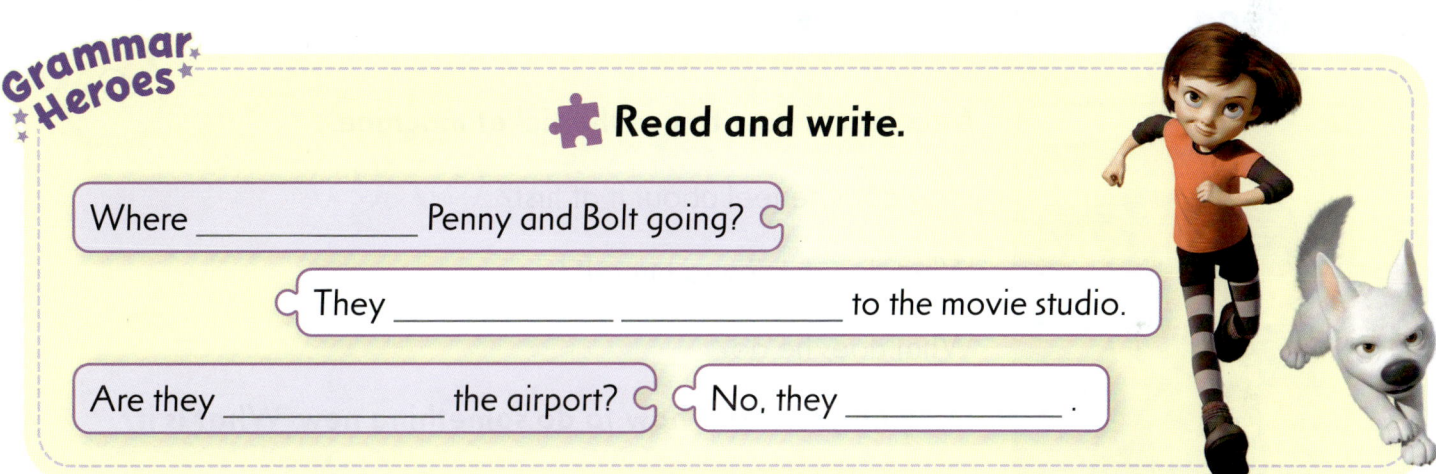

Grammar Heroes

Read and write.

Where _____ Penny and Bolt going?

They _____ _____ to the movie studio.

Are they _____ the airport?

No, they _____ .

2 Look, read, and write.

❶ Where ___is he going___ ?
_____ the market.

❷ Is she _____ the circus?
Yes, _____ .

Extra time?
Think of you going to a place. Ask and answer.

I can talk about where people are going.

67

A journey and a surprise

**LESSON 4
Story**

1 Remember the story. Circle *T* (True) or *F* (False).

1. Tom is Max's brother. T / F
2. The children find a school on the map. T / F
3. The bus leaves at quarter after ten. T / F
4. At first, Max can't use the ticket machine. T / F

2 Read and write.

1. Who gives the children cards? ___Tom___
2. Who likes learning from pictures? _____
3. Who finds what time the bus leaves? _____
4. Who asks a woman for help? _____

Diego   Max
Sato   Uma
~~Tom~~

3 Read, circle, and write. Then compare with a friend.

Max learns how to use the ticket machine.

How does he feel about it at first? 😊 ☹️

What does he say to himself? _____

What does he do? _____

Imagine you learn how to do something new. What is it?

How do you feel about doing this thing? 😊 ☹️

What do you say to yourself? _____

What do you do? _____

My favorite scene in the story is _____ because _____.

Storytellers club

Extra time?
Imagine you are Max. Retell the story.

> We are in town with my brother Tom …

I can read a story about learning new things.

LESSON 5
Vocabulary and Grammar

1 Read, look, and match.

1. They're going to school on foot. `d`
2. He's going to work by van. ☐
3. They're going to school by taxi. ☐
4. She's going home by motorcycle. ☐
5. He's going home by subway. ☐
6. She's going to work by helicopter. ☐

2 Follow and write.

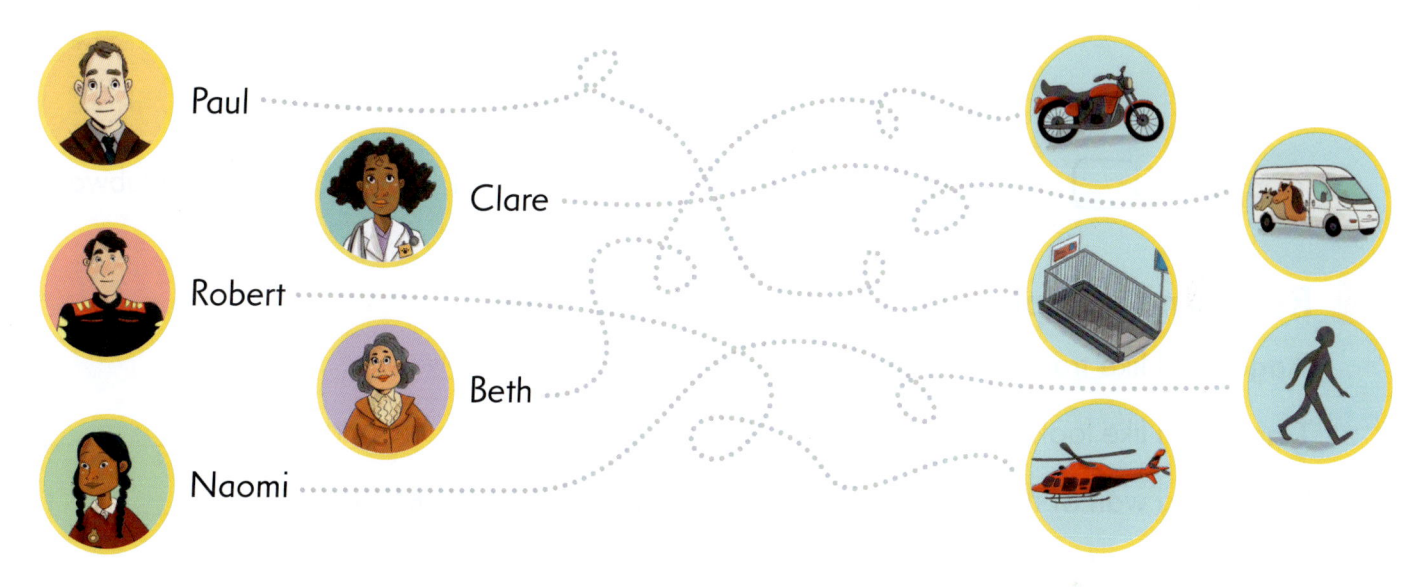

Paul _goes to work by subway_ .
Clare _____ .
Robert _____ .

Beth _____ .
Naomi _____ school on _____ .

3 Look at 2. Write questions and answers.

1. How does Paul go to work?   He goes by subway.
2. _____ _____
3. _____ _____
4. _____ _____
5. _____ _____

⏲ **Extra time?**

Make picture cards for the new words.

I can talk about traveling to school and work.

69

LESSON 6
Listening and Speaking

1 🎧 Listen and check (✓). Then write the total number of people.

	by bus	by taxi	on foot	by subway
Mark			✓	
Tina				
Pedro				
Angelo				

ⓐ by bus ☐   ⓑ by taxi ☐   ⓒ on foot ☐ 1   ⓓ by subway ☐

2 Read and complete.

Angelo: I like trains. They are fast. I go to the park ___by subway___ .

Tina: I like looking at people and buildings. I always walk to the park. I go _____ .

Pedro: I wait at the bus stop. The bus comes every ten minutes. I go _____ .

Mark: I walk to the park with Tina. It's good exercise. I go _____ .

3 💬 Complete the survey for you. Then ask and answer.

	by bus	by taxi	on foot	by subway
school				
movie theater				
park				
home from school				

How do you go to school?

I go by car.

❶ How do you go to the movie theater? _____

❷ _____ to the park? _____

🕐 **Extra time?**

Imagine you are a famous person. How do you go to work?

I can do a survey about transportation.

LESSON 7
Myself and others
Self-awareness

Learning new things

1 Read and choose one challenge.

Try something new!

- Write the alphabet with your opposite hand.
- With your eyes closed, walk from your bedroom to the kitchen. 
- Make something useful with string, glue, and paper. 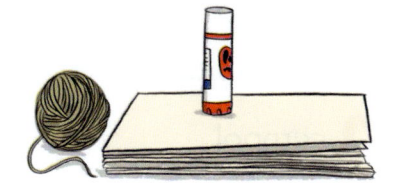

2 Now try it! Then read and write.

1. How do you feel? _____
2. What strategies do you use? _____
3. Do you ask for help? _____

My portfolio

3 Draw a *Keep learning* tree.
Write the four top learning strategies in your tree.

Be a hero!
Keep a diary of the new things you try.

I can keep trying to learn new things.

71

LESSON 8
My world

Green transportation

1 Read and match.

1. green transportation
2. public transportation
3. electric car
4. carpool

a. We use this with other people, for example, buses and trains.
b. Using this keeps our planet clean.
c. This is when you share a car with other people.
d. We can drive this but it doesn't use gas.

2 Look and write. Are these forms of transportation green? Why?

coal   gas   ~~the sun~~   the wind

1. Yes, because it uses energy from the sun.
2. _____
3. _____
4. _____

3 Invent a form of green transportation. Write, draw, and label.

How does it work? wind / sun / electricity / water / other _____

Why is it green? _____

What do the different parts do?

Extra time?
Think about your new invention. Where can you go with it?

I can read and talk about green transportation.

72

A transportation infographic

LESSON 9
Project

1 Use the information to complete the infographic.

the park – survey of 10 children
walk III
bike IIII
bus I
car II

How we travel to _____

👣 ☐ children go on foot

4 _____ go by _____

🚌 ☐ child goes by _____

2 _____ go by _____

2 Think about your infographic. Draw pictures and make notes.

How we travel: _____

_____ 5 children go by bus

_____

Let's go _____ .

_____

_____

Check!

There are short, interesting headings. ○

There isn't too much information. ○

3 Reflect on your project.

My infographic is easy to understand:
☆☆☆☆☆

I use pictures to help me remember the information:
☆☆☆☆☆

My infographic
Who do you ask in your survey? _____
What different transportation is in your survey? _____
Do lots of children use green transportation? _____

I can make a transportation infographic.

73

**LESSON 10
Review**

My progress journal

1 **Read and match.**

1. I walk
2. Cars and buses
3. We can buy food
4. We can take a bus
5. My sister goes to work
6. Jenny takes the subway

a. at the bus station.
b. by motorcycle.
c. on the sidewalk.
d. travel on roads.
e. to get to work.
f. at the market.

2 **Look, read, and write.**

1. ___How does___ Uma's mom go to work?
She goes ___by helicopter___.

2. _____ Uma's dad go to work?
He _____.

3 **What I know.**

Write. What transportation do you usually use?

_____

Say. Talk about this scene from the video. What happens? Do you like it?

Star progress

- This unit was ☆☆☆☆☆
- My favorite lesson is _____
  because _____.
- I can now _____.

UNIT 6
Exam practice

Listening

1 🎧 6.3 **Listen, color, and write.**

Reading

2 **Read, choose, and write. Then check (✔).**

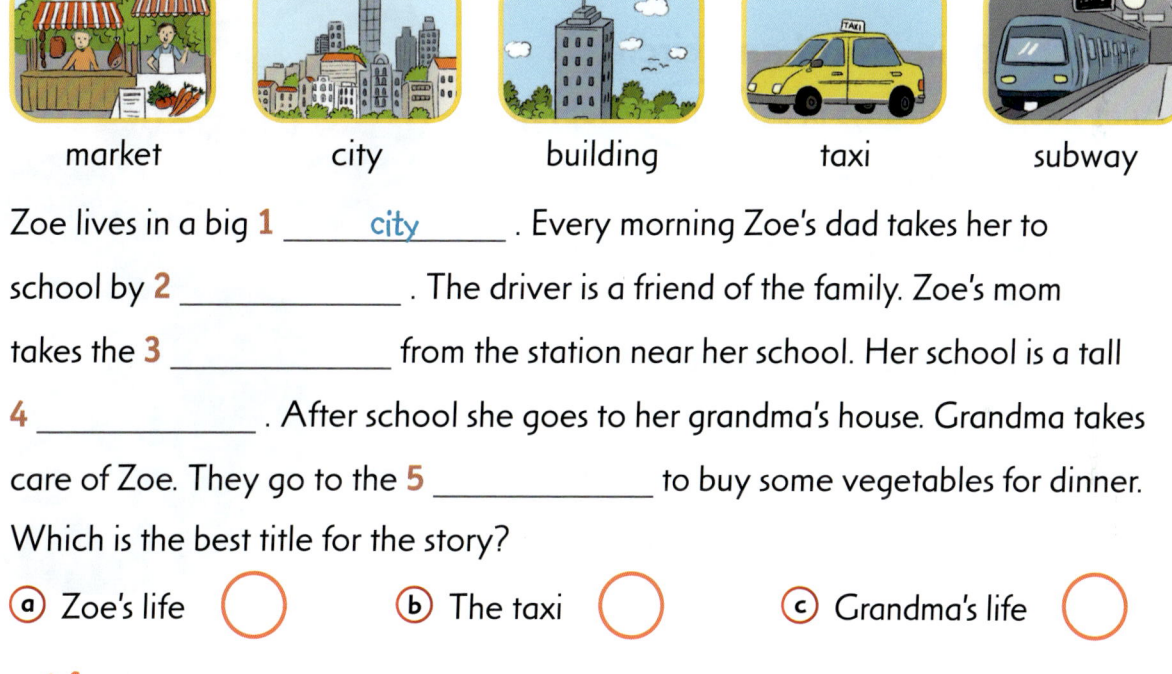

market   city   building   taxi   subway

Zoe lives in a big **1** ___city___ . Every morning Zoe's dad takes her to school by **2** _____ . The driver is a friend of the family. Zoe's mom takes the **3** _____ from the station near her school. Her school is a tall **4** _____ . After school she goes to her grandma's house. Grandma takes care of Zoe. They go to the **5** _____ to buy some vegetables for dinner.

Which is the best title for the story?

ⓐ Zoe's life ○   ⓑ The taxi ○   ⓒ Grandma's life ○

Speaking

3 💬 **Answer the questions for you.**

How do you go to school?

Where are you going this weekend?

Do you like the circus?

How does your mom or dad go to work?

Do you use the subway?

7 Things at home

Learning Heroes

I want to learn new words about things at home:

_____
_____
_____

Draw: a thing I want to give away

I want to:
- a story
- about things at home
- Toy Story 3 video
- about using things again

Video quiz

1 **Watch again. Read and circle.**

1. Andy keeps his old toys in a **(toy box)** / **laptop**.
2. Andy's old toys **can** / **can't** talk.
3. Andy **wants** / **doesn't want** to give his old toys to Sunnyside.
4. Mom thinks the **black bag** / **toy box** with Andy's toys is trash.
5. Bonnie's wearing yellow boots and **a necklace** / **glasses**.
6. Andy loves Woody. Bonnie loves **Woody** / **Andy**, too.

2 **Read and circle T (True) or F (False). Then write for you.**

Molly gives away some of her old toys to Sunnyside Day Center.   T / F

Andy gives his favorite old toy, Woody, to Bonnie.   T / F

What old toys can you give away? _____

76

LESSON 1 Vocabulary

3 Find, circle, and write.

1. laptop
2. _____
3. _____
4. _____

n e c k l a c e **l a p t o p** t o y b o x m a g a z i n e

4 Read and write words from 3.

1. I can play games on this.   laptop
2. I can wear this.   _____
3. I put my toys in this.   _____
4. I can read this.   _____

Challenge!
Find 6 letters in orange.
Then guess the word.
_____

Extra time?
Look in your toy box.
What's your favorite toy?
Draw and write.

I can name things at home.

77

LESSON 2
Vocabulary

1 Look, read, and match.

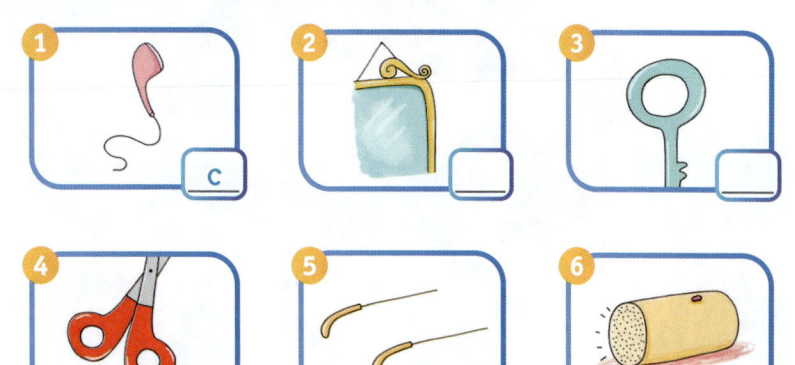

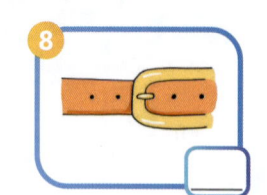

a) My belt is brown and yellow.
b) Mom is wearing a bracelet.
c) I listen to music with my earphones.
d) This is the key to my house.
e) I have a mirror in my bedroom.
f) There's a radio in the kitchen.
g) We can use scissors to cut paper.
h) My sunglasses have stars on them.

2 Look, read, and write. What's missing? Look at 1 and write.

Find out!
Are there any special clothes that come from your country? When do people wear them?

1. Clara is wearing ___a bracelet___ .
2. She is also _____ .
3. Clara has _____ in her hand.
4. She also has _____ .
What word is missing? _____

5. Li Wei is wearing _____ .
6. He is also _____ .
7. Li Wei has _____ in his hand.

Extra time?
What things can you see in your room? Say.

I can name things at home.

LESSON 3
Grammar

1 🎧 Listen and number.

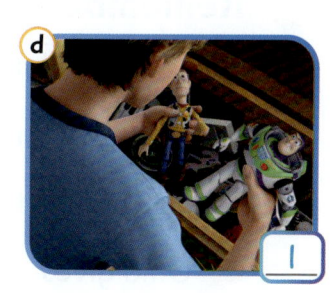

a b c d

Grammar Heroes

🧩 Read and write.

_____ necklace is this?

It's hers.

Whose toys are _____ ?

They're _____ .

2 Complete column 1 for you. Then think of two friends and complete columns 2 and 3. Then write.

	Me	_____	_____
earphones	✔		
magazine			
mirror			
scissors			

1. ____Whose____ earphones are these? They're ____mine____ .
2. _____ magazine is this? It's _____ .
3. Whose _____ ? _____
4. _____ They're _____ .

⏰ **Extra time?**

Choose three things in your classroom. Whose are they? Ask and answer.

I can and answer questions about who things belong to.

79

Use it again!

**LESSON 4
Story**

1 Remember the story. Read and match.

1. Zoe and Uma — d
2. They look in a box
3. Uma wants to keep
4. Uma gives
5. The children
6. Cleo uses the box

a. fix the box.
b. again as a bed.
c. of old things.
d. are sisters.
e. her sunglasses.
f. her bracelet to Sato.

2 Number in order.

a. Sato wants to help. She likes looking at old things.
b. Zoe finds a box of old things.
c. Uma wants to keep the sunglasses because they're funny.
d. Sato doesn't put the box in the trash.
e. The children are at Uma and Zoe's house. [1]
f. Cleo uses the box as a bed.
g. Sato likes bracelets. Uma gives Sato the bracelet.

3 Read, write, and circle. Then compare with a friend.

Uma gives away her _____ and her _____ .

Sato feels 🙂 ☹ .

Uma uses her _____ again.

Imagine you are looking at your old things. What do you do?

I give away my _____ .

I feel 🙂 ☹ .

I use my _____ again.

I **like** / **don't like** the story because _____ .

Storytellers club

Extra time?

Think of one of your old things. Can you fix it or give it away to a friend?

I can read a story about using things again.

80

LESSON 5
Vocabulary and Grammar

1 🎧 7.2 **Listen, find, and color.**

2 Look at 1. Read and write.

above   by   inside   beside   on top of   below

- _Where's_ the shelf?
- It's ___by___ the armchair.

- _____ the armchair?
- It's _____ the radio.

- _____ the shelf?
- It's _____ the radio.

- _____ the drawers?
- They're _____ the cupboard.

- _____ the mirror?
- _____ the cupboard.

- _____ the flowers?
- _____ the armchair.

3 Look at 1. Complete and write two more sentences.

1. The books are _on top of the shelf._
2. The cat is _____.
3. _____.
4. _____.

⏱ **Extra time?**
Look at your classroom.
What can you see? Where?
Write sentences.

I can ask and answer questions about where things are.

81

LESSON 6
Listening and Speaking

1 🎧 7.3 **Listen and write. Then look. Where's the lamp?**
1. The keys are ____below____ the shelf.
2. The scissors are _____ the drawer.
3. The bracelet is _____ the table.
4. The magazine is _____ the shelf.

2 Put the words in order to make answers. Then look and match.
1. Where are the sunglasses?
   inside / They're / the / drawer.
   They're inside the drawer.   [a]
2. Where's the shelf?
   It's / the / above / cupboard.
   _____   [ ]
3. Where's the radio?
   beside / the / It's / stairs.
   _____   [ ]
4. Where's the cushion?
   the / on top of / It's / armchair.
   _____   [ ]

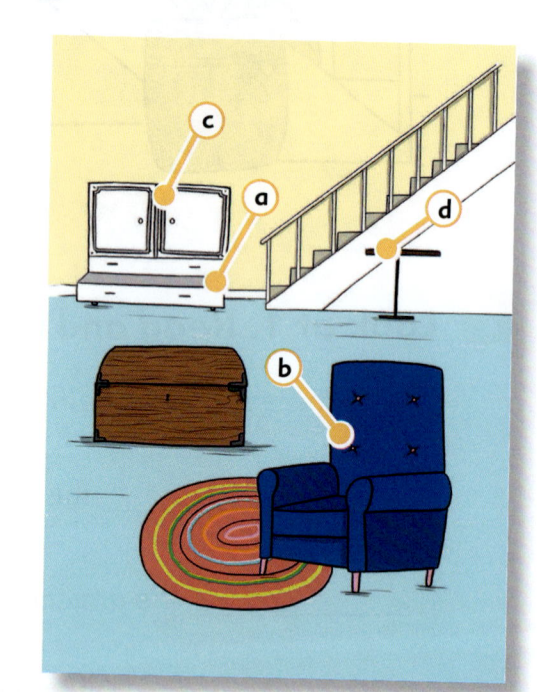

3 💬 **Draw. Then ask and answer.**

armchair   belt   bracelet   cushions   magazines   shelf   toy box

Where's the lamp?
It's on top of the desk.

⏰ **Extra time?**
Describe your room to a friend. Your friend draws the room without looking at your picture.

I can talk about where things are in a room.

82

LESSON 7
Myself and others
Responsible decision-making

Using things again

1 Do the quiz. What's your score?

What do you do with old things?

1. When my radio doesn't work, I …
   - a put it in the trash.
   - b fix it.

2. When I don't use my toys, I …
   - a keep them.
   - b give them away.

3. When I sometimes use my sunglasses, I …
   - a put them in the trash.
   - b keep them.

4. When my clothes are small, I …
   - a put them in the trash.
   - b give them away.

5. When my clothes are old, I …
   - a put them in the trash.
   - b fix them.

6. When I finish reading a magazine, I …
   - a keep it.
   - b give it away.

Add your points!
As = 0 point
Bs = 1 point

Your score:
1–2 Think about why it is good to use things again.
3–4 Very good. You are good at using things again but can do a little better.
5–6 Excellent! You are good at using things again and making others happy.

2 Read and write. Use the phrases in 1 to help you.

1. These earphones don't work. _Fix them!_
2. I never use this belt. _____
3. I love this bracelet. It's special. _____
4. The radio doesn't work. _____

My portfolio

3 Make a *Use it again!* poster. Look, draw, and write.

It's good to use things again!

Item: _____   Item: _____   Item: _____

Keep _____   Fix _____   Give away _____

Be a hero!
Make a list of the things you can fix or give away. How many are there?

I can talk about using things again.

Electrical circuits

**LESSON 8
My world**

1 Look, choose, and label. Then read and write.

battery   circuit   switch   wire

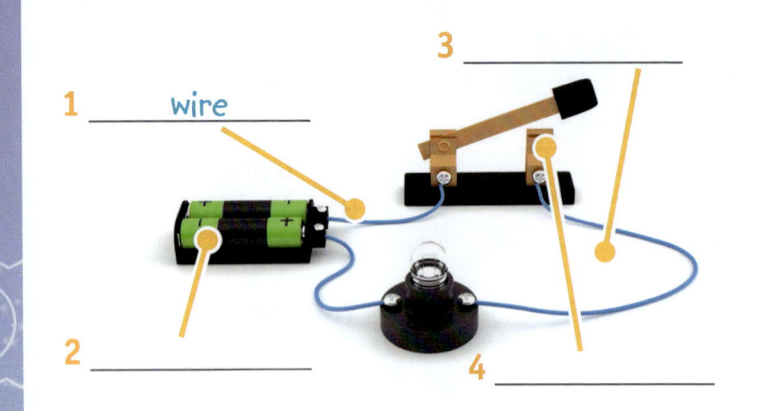

1 ___wire___
2 _____
3 _____
4 _____

How does a **5** _____ work? First you turn on the **6** _____ to close the circuit. Then the energy from the **7** _____ goes through the **8** _____ and turns on the light.

2 Look and write. How can you make these things work?

1. The robot has a ___switch___, a _____ and it has two _____ . The switch is on. We need one more _____ to make a circuit.

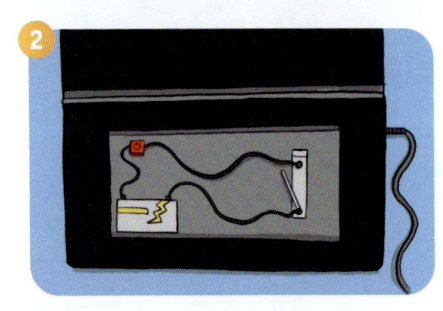

2. The laptop has a _____ , a _____ and _____ . The switch is off. We need to _____ the switch to make a circuit.

3 Think of a toy that has a circuit. Draw the circuit and write.

This is a toy _____ .
The circuit has a _____ , _____ and a _____ . The switch is _____ .

Extra time?
Look in your classroom. Find something that works with a circuit. What is it?

I can read and talk about electrical circuits.

84

LESSON 9
Project

My ideal bedroom

1 Think about your ideal bedroom. Draw and write.

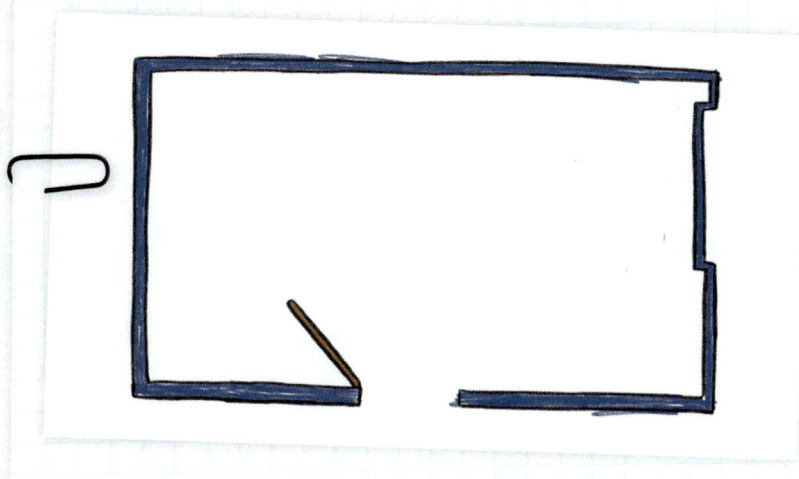

What things are in your bedroom?
What color and size are they?
Where are they?

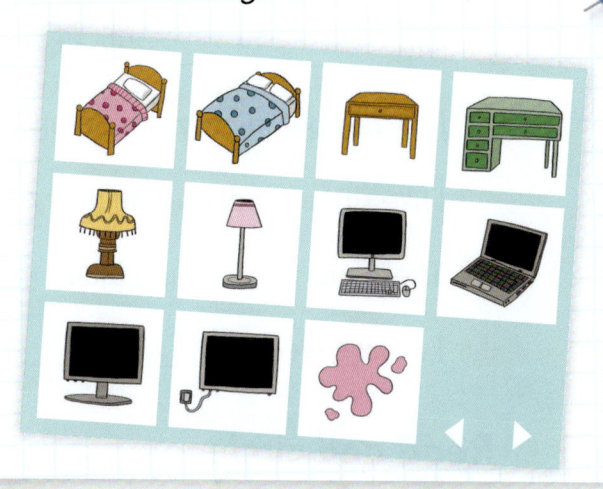

The bed is big and brown. It's by …

_____

_____

2 Look, choose advice, and write. Then practice your presentation.

Stand up straight!   Relax!   Point to the pictures!

1    2    3

_____   _____   _____
_____   _____   _____

Check!

There are prepositions: *above, below, inside, on top of, beside, by.*

There are interesting adjectives.

3 Reflect on your project.

I point to the pictures on my poster:
☆☆☆☆☆

I stand up straight:
☆☆☆☆☆

My ideal bedroom

Do you have lots of color in your ideal bedroom?
_____

Are all the things you want in your ideal bedroom?
_____

Where is your favorite thing in your ideal bedroom?
_____

I can design and present my ideal bedroom.

85

**LESSON 10
Review**

My progress journal

1 Read, choose, and write.

> armchair   bracelet   cushions   earphones   ~~magazine~~   toy box

1. My __magazine__ about animals is on top of the shelf.
2. My _____ don't work. I can't hear the music!
3. I always put my toys inside my _____ !
4. I like sitting and reading in my _____ .
5. There are two red and blue _____ beside the bed.
6. I always wear this _____ on my arm — it's my grandpa's.

2 Read and circle.

1. (**Whose**) / **What** toys are these? They're **you** / **yours**.
2. They're Sarah's scissors. They're **mine** / **hers**.
3. Dad has a blue belt. It's **theirs** / **his**.
4. **Whose** / **Where** is the laptop? It's **my** / **mine**.

3 What I know.

Write. Describe your favorite thing in your home.
Where is it? _____

Say. Talk about this scene from the video.
What happens? Do you like it?

Star progress

- This unit was ☆☆☆☆☆
- My favorite lesson is _____
  because _____ .
- I can now _____ .

86

UNIT 7
Exam practice

Listening

1 🎧 7.4 **Listen and check (✔).**

1. Where are the earphones?
   a b ✔ c

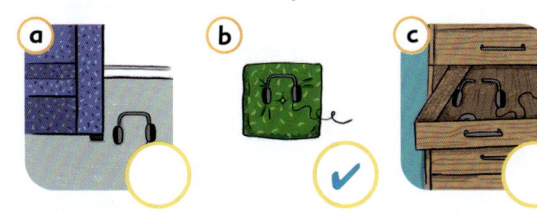

2. Where is the mirror?
   a b c

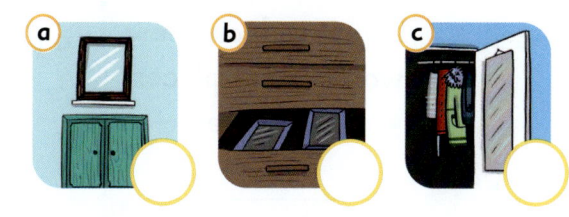

3. Which cushion is Mom talking about?
   a b c

4. Whose scissors are these?
   a b c

Reading

2 Read, choose, and write.

Tom's house has a big living room. There's a blue **1** _armchair_ with a cushion on it. It's **2** _____ a shelf with books on. There is a mirror **3** _____ the shelf, too. The books are his mom's, they aren't **4** _____ . Next to the armchair is a **5** _____ with three drawers. There's a bracelet **6** _____ the first drawer. It's his sister's bracelet – it's **7** _____ .

1. stairs   earphone   (armchair)
2. inside   below   above
3. outside   inside   on top of
4. hers   ours   his

5. magazine   armchair   cupboard
6. above   inside   below
7. she   hers   yours

Speaking

3 💬 **Look at the pictures in 1. Say what is different.**

8 On a journey

Learning Heroes

I want to learn new words about places in nature:

_____
_____
_____

Draw: a place in nature

I want to:
- a story
- about nature and the weather
- The Good Dinosaur video
- about how to manage fears

Video quiz

1 Watch again. Circle *T* (True) or *F* (False).
1. Arlo and his family are dinosaurs. **T** / F
2. Arlo has a brother and a sister. T / F
3. Poppa doesn't help Arlo. T / F
4. Arlo doesn't fall off the mountain. T / F
5. Spot is in danger in the river. T / F
6. Arlo puts his footprint on the wall. T / F

2 Read and complete. Then write for you.

Poppa   Arlo

1. _____ is scared of everything at the beginning of the movie.
2. _____ shows Arlo that the world isn't always scary.
3. I'm scared of _____ . I'm not scared of _____ .

88

LESSON 1 **Vocabulary**

3 Look and write.

1. __mountains__
2. _____
3. _____
4. _____

Challenge!

Circle. Then write the missing word.

m	o	u	n	t	a	i	n	s
i	r	w	o	o	d	s	e	l
c	l	o	u	d	s	y	o	p

_____

4 Look at 3. Read and write.

1. The __mountains__ are white, brown, and green.
2. The _____ are white and pink.
3. The _____ is blue.
4. The _____ are green and brown.

Extra time?

Look outside. What can you see?

I can see clouds.
I can't see mountains.

I can name things in nature.

89

LESSON 2
Vocabulary

1 Look and match.

1. There's a path. **c**
2. There's a cave.
3. There's an open gate.
4. There's a volcano.
5. There are some flowers in a field.
6. There's a river in the valley.
7. There's a waterfall.
8. There are animals on a farm.

2 Look at 1. Read and write. Where are they?

1. Lily is at her grandparents' ____farm____ . She can see yellow flowers in the _____ .
2. Sam is opening a _____ . He's walking on a _____ through the woods.
3. Hannah is in a _____ with a river. She's standing next to a _____ .
4. Andy can see a _____ with fire and rocks.
   There's a small _____ , too.

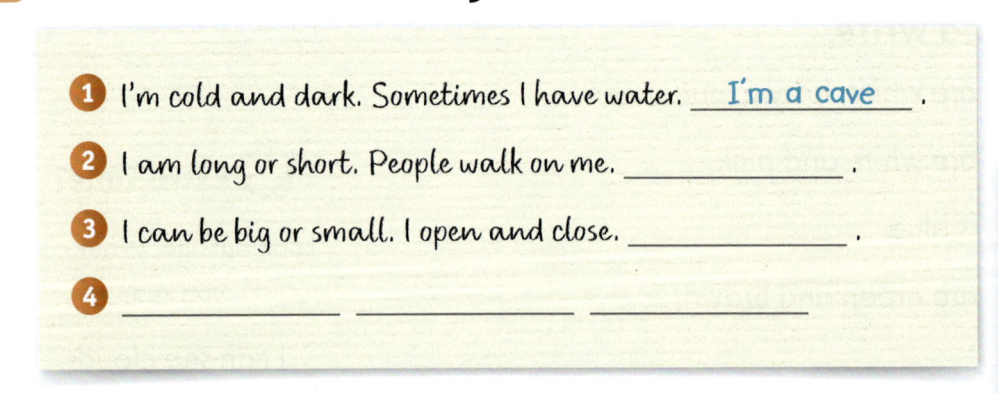

Find out!
Find out about a real volcano. What's it called? Where is it? How old is it?

3 What am I? Read and guess. Then write one more.

1. I'm cold and dark. Sometimes I have water. __I'm a cave__ .
2. I am long or short. People walk on me. _____ .
3. I can be big or small. I open and close. _____ .
4. _____ _____ _____

Extra time?
Are there any farms, fields, valleys, or waterfalls near your home?

I can name things in nature.

90

LESSON 3
Grammar

1 🎧 8.1 **Listen, circle, and match.**

1. On Arlo's journey, there **were some / weren't any** clouds. There **were some / weren't any** stars.

2. There **was / wasn't** a gate. There **was / wasn't** a path.

3. There **was / wasn't** a valley in the countryside. There **was / wasn't** a field.

4. There **were some / weren't any** volcanoes on his journey. There **were some / weren't any** mountains.

a [ ]   b [1]
c [ ]   d [ ]

Grammar Heroes

🧩 **Read and write.**

On Arlo's journey, there _____ some woods.

There _____ a valley.

2 Imagine you are on a journey. Check (✓) what you see. Then write.

○   ○   ○   ○   ○   ○

On my journey, there was _____ .

There wasn't _____ .

At night, there were _____ .

There weren't _____ .

_____ .

⏱ Extra time?

Describe your journey to a friend.

> There weren't any stars. There were some fields.

I can talk about what there was in the past.

An exciting day

LESSON 4 Story

1 Remember the story. Read, choose, and write.

> cave   Diego   help   river   waterfalls   ~~woods~~

The children are visiting the **1** ___woods___ with Tom. There's a river and two **2** _____ . Suddenly, they hear thunder! The children hide in the **3** _____ , but Cleo is having fun! **4** _____ feels scared. He counts to five and feels calm. Suddenly, Cleo is in the **5** _____ ! She can't swim. Diego can **6** _____ . He pulls Cleo out of the river.

2 Who says it? Read and match.

Come on! I know the way!
___Tom___

Let's hide in that cave!
_____

Uma, I'm scared of storms.
_____

Yes! I can do it!
_____

> Diego   Uma   Sato   ~~Tom~~

3 What makes you feel scared? Write for Diego. Then imagine and write for you. Compare with a friend.

Diego's journal
I'm in the woods. It's raining.
I don't like storms. I feel _____ .
I breath _____ and _____ .
Then I _____ to five.
Now I feel _____ .

My journal
I'm _____ .
I don't like _____ .
I feel _____ .
I _____ .
Now I feel calm.

I think the story is _____ because _____ .

Storytellers club

I can read a story about managing fear.

Extra time? Write a different ending to the story. What happens to Cleo and Diego?

LESSON 5
Vocabulary and Grammar

1 🎧 8.2 **Read, choose, and write. Then listen and check.**

~~fog~~   lightning   rainbow   stars   storm   thunder

⚓ **Log in** | **Ship log** | **Reports** | **Archives**

Day 1
The weather wasn't good today. There was a lot of 1 _____fog_____ .

Night 1
The weather was great! There weren't any clouds in the sky. There were a lot of 2 _____ .

Day 2
There was a bad 3 _____ today. There was 4 _____ and 5 _____ .

Day 3
It was a beautiful day! There was some rain. Then there was a beautiful 6 _____ in the sky.

2 **Look, read, and circle.**

1. Was there any fog? **Yes, there was.** / **(No, there wasn't.)**
2. **Was there** / **Were there** any clouds? No, there weren't.
3. Were there any stars? **Yes, there were.** / **No, there weren't.**
4. **Was there** / **Were there** a waterfall? No, there wasn't.
5. Was there a rainbow? **Yes, there was.** / **No, there wasn't.**

3 **Look at 1 and write.**

Girl: How was your journey?
Captain: The weather wasn't always good. On the first day 1 ___there was___ a lot of fog.
Girl: 2 _____ any clouds at night?
Captain: No, 3 _____ .
Girl: 4 _____ any stars?
Captain: 5 _____ .

⏱ **Extra time?**
Think of a place in nature and make a web diagram.

I can ask and answer questions about what there was in the past.

93

LESSON 6
Listening and Speaking

1 🎧 8.3 **Listen and circle. Then match.**

① There **was** / **wasn't** a storm yesterday. There **was** / **wasn't** thunder. There **was** / **wasn't** lightning.

② I **was** / **wasn't** in the woods on the weekend. There **were some** / **weren't any** mountains. There **were some** / **weren't any** waterfalls. There **was** / **wasn't** a rainbow.

2 **Put the words in order to make questions. Then answer and check (✓).**

① a farm / there / Was / ?

Was there a farm? Yes, _there was_ .

② there / Was / a gate / ?

_____ No, _____ .

③ mountains / there / any / Were / ?

_____ No, _____ .

④ there / a field / Was / ?

_____ Yes, _____ .

3 💬 **Complete and color. Then write. Ask and answer.**

Was there a farm?

No, there wasn't.

There was a river.   _There were some stars in the sky._

_____   _____

⏱ **Extra time?**

Think of some more questions to ask about your friend's camping trip.

94   **I can** ask and answer about what there was on a camping trip.

LESSON 7
Myself and others
Self-management

Managing your fears

1 💡 Imagine you are one of the children. Write *F* (Feel) or *D* (Do).

1. I'm hot and my legs are shaking. **F**
2. I read a book.
3. I want to cry.
4. I talk to a friend or a person in my family.
5. My stomach feels funny.
6. I'm breathing very fast.
7. I take deep breaths and I count to five.
8. I want to run away.

2 💡 💬 How useful are these calm down strategies? Number them 1 to 5. Then write two more. Compare with a friend.

a. Talk to a friend.
b. Count to five.
c. Draw or color.
d. Go for a walk.
e. Listen to music.
f. _____
g. _____

My portfolio

3 💡 What calm down strategies do you use? Think and write.

I'm scared of: _____

Calm Down Stars

Be a hero! Find someone who is scared of the same thing as you.

I can manage my fears.

Earth Science

Dinosaurs

**LESSON 8
My world**

1 Look and match.

1
2

a. The shape of the bones of an animal in a rock makes a fossil.

b. Mud, sand, and rock make layers in the mountains.

2 What are these fossils? Look, match, and write.

1
2

a. This is a fossil of a _____ .
We can see its head and long body.

b. This is a fossil of a _____ .
We can see its mouth and tail.

crab   shark   turtle

3 Choose a sea creature and find pictures of its fossils. Draw and write.

A 1 _____ dies and 2 _____ covers its bones.

A lot of mud, 3 _____ , and rock cover the bones. It all turns into rock.

4 _____ goes into the bones and makes a fossil shape.

Seas dry up over millions of years. Scientists 5 _____ for the fossils of sea creatures in the ground, on the beach or even on top of mountains!

Extra time?
Label the body parts in your fossil picture.

I can read and write about fossils.

A comic book story

LESSON 9
Project

1 🎧 **Listen, read, and circle.**

① Maria is talking and Joe **starts** / **doesn't start** talking. Joe **is** / **isn't** taking turns to talk.

② Joe **waits** / **doesn't wait** for Maria to finish talking. He **is** / **isn't** taking turns to talk.

③ Enzo **works** / **doesn't work** together. He asks Joe, **"What do you think?"** / **"What do you want?"**

2 💬 **In groups, complete your comic book story plan. Then draw and write.**

Heading: _____

Characters:
_____
_____
_____
_____

Place: _____

Time: _____

Check!

There's a sentence above each picture to say what's happening. ◯

The words people say are in speech bubbles. ◯

3 **Reflect on your project.**

I take turns to talk:
☆ ☆ ☆ ☆ ☆

I ask others, "What do you think?":
☆ ☆ ☆ ☆ ☆

My comic book story

Who are your characters? _____
What are they doing? _____
Where are they? _____

I can work in a group to create a comic book story.

LESSON 10
Review

My progress journal

1 Read and circle.

1. There were clouds in the **(sky)** / **mountain**.
2. There was a **cave** / **gate** in front of a path.
3. There were animals in the **field** / **volcano**.
4. There was a colorful **waterfall** / **rainbow** in the sky.
5. At night there were **fog** / **stars** in the sky.
6. There wasn't any **thunder** / **clouds** or lightning.

2 Read and write.

1. I was in the woods. There __were some__ mountains. There _____ waterfalls.
2. _____ fields?
3. No, _____ .
4. _____ cave?
5. Yes, _____ .

3 What I know.

Write. Describe your favorite journey.

_____
_____

Say. Talk about this scene from the video. What happens? Do you like it?

Star progress

- This unit was ☆☆☆☆☆
- My favorite lesson is _____
  because _____ .
- I can now _____ .

UNIT 8
Exam practice

Listening

1 🎧 **Listen and write a letter in each box.**

her dad	her brother	her sister	her grandma	her grandpa
c				

a b  c  d  e

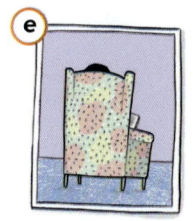

Reading and Writing

2 Read and choose.

1. Where were you yesterday, Tony?
   - a) Yes, I was.
   - **(b) I was in the mountains.**
   - c) I am in the mountains.

2. Was there a star in the sky?
   - a) Yes, there is.
   - b) Yes, there were.
   - c) No, there wasn't.

3. Where was the rainbow?
   - a) I like rainbows.
   - b) It was in the sky.
   - c) They are in the sky.

4. I don't like storms.
   - a) I do!
   - b) No, I don't.
   - c) Yes, I do.

Speaking

3 💬 **Answer the questions for you.**

Where do you usually go on vacation?

How do you get there?

Do you like storms? Why? / Why not?

Were there any clouds this morning?

9 Telling stories

Learning Heroes

I want to learn new words for characters in stories:

_____
_____
_____

Draw: a place in a story

I want to:
- a story
- about stories
- Tangled video
- about how to make new friends

Video quiz

1 Watch again. Read, choose, and write.

animals   dance   ~~different~~   friends   games   party   singing   town

Rapunzel has lots of 1 _____different_____ friends. Rapunzel asks her new 2 _____ in the restaurant what they like doing. They all like 3 _____ . Rapunzel goes into the 4 _____ and makes new friends, and they 5 _____ together. Rapunzel is friends with 6 _____ , too. She plays 7 _____ with her lizard, Pascal. In the end, Rapunzel has a 8 _____ with her family and friends. Everyone is happy!

2 Read and circle. Then write for you.

1. Rapunzel sings a song with people in **the restaurant** / **town**.
2. She dances with the people in **the restaurant** / **town**.
3. How are your friends different from you? _____

LESSON 1 Vocabulary

3 Look, circle, and write.

q u e e n k i n g p r i n c e s s p r i n c e

1. _____
2. _____
3. queen
4. _____

Challenge!
Find 4 letters in orange. Then guess the word.
_____

4 Read and write. Who's missing?

1. Rapunzel is the _____ .
2. Rapunzel's mom is the _____ .
3. Rapunzel's dad is the _____ .
4. The _____ is missing.

Extra time?
Make a list of any kings, queens, princes, and princesses you know.

I can name characters in a story.

101

LESSON 2
Vocabulary

1 **Follow the path and number in order.**

a. There are slides in the castle. ☐
b. People are climbing the tall tower. ☐
c. There are stores in the town center. ☐
d. There are beautiful flowers in the secret garden. ☐
e. People are playing in the jungle. ☐
f. People are flying in the spaceships. ☐
g. There's a movie about another planet. ☐
h. People are having fun on the pirate ship. ☐ 1

2 **Read, look, and write.**

Pete's home is 1 _in the town center_.

He lives 2 _____. His bedroom is

3 _____. He plays 4 _____

with his friends. He loves walking 5 _____

because he can see lots of animals. Pete's mom is an actor.

Today she's a pirate. She is 6 _____.

Pete wants to live 7 _____.

He can go there 8 _____.

Find out!
Can people live on another planet? Why? / Why not?

Extra time?
Read and guess. Then write one for your friend to guess.
You can take this to go to the moon or to another planet. What is it?

I can name places in a story.

102

LESSON 3
Grammar

1 Listen and check (✓). Where were they?

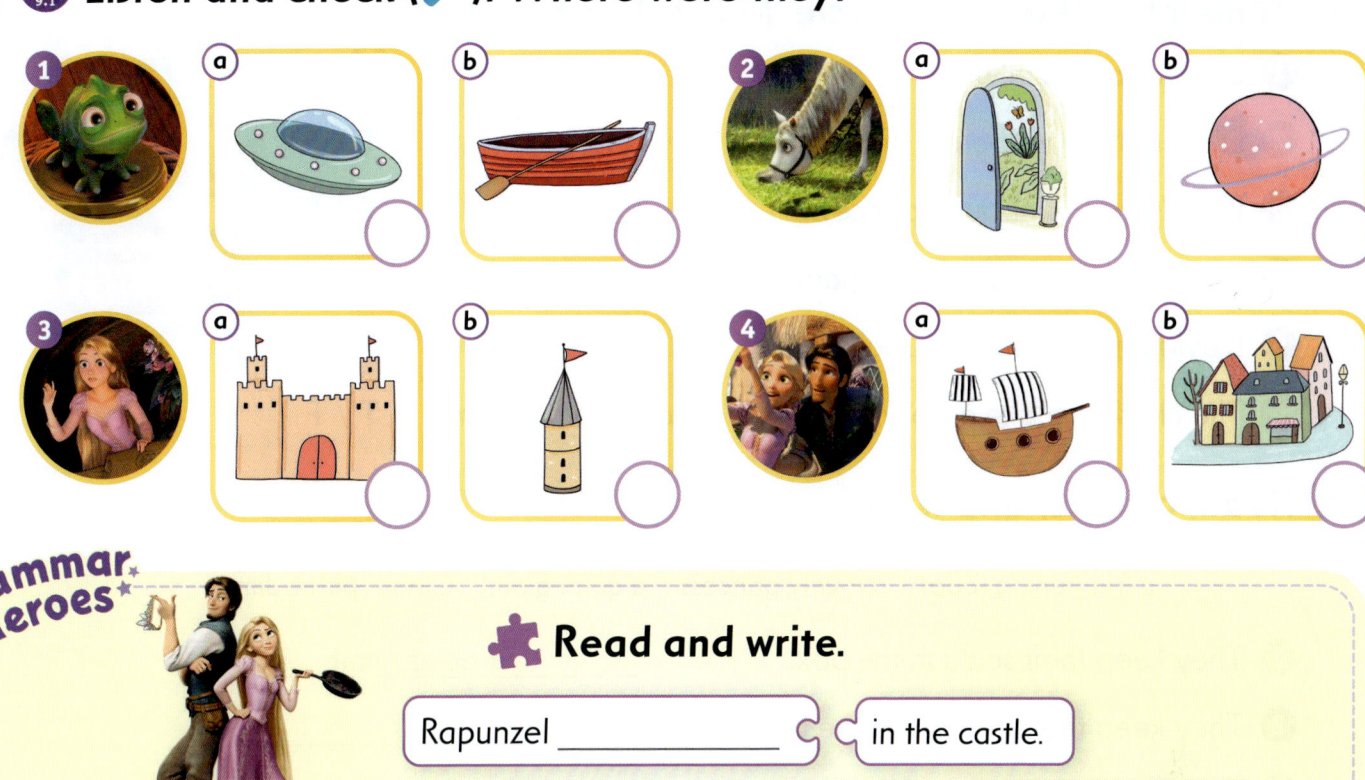

Grammar Heroes

Read and write.

Rapunzel _____ in the castle.

The people _____ in the town centre.

2 Look at 1. Read and write. Then write for you.

① Pascal ___was___ on the boat.

He _wasn't in the spaceship_ .

② Maximus _____ in the secret garden.

He _____ .

③ Rapunzel _____ in the castle.

She _____ .

④ Eugene and Rapunzel _____ on the pirate ship.

They _____ .

⑤ Yesterday, my family and I _____ .

_____

Extra time?

Imagine you were in an exciting place with your family. Ask and answer.

Where were you?

We were in a tower. We weren't at an RV park.

I can say where people were and weren't in the past.

103

A special box

**LESSON 4
Story**

1 Remember the story. Circle *T* (True) or *F* (False).

1. Zoe has a special box. (T)/ F
2. Li Mei's story is about a pirate ship. T / F
3. Pablo's story is about a princess. T / F
4. Lisa's story is about a quiet giant. T / F
5. David's story is about a spaceship. T / F
6. The children make a story book called *Stories with Friends*. T / F

2 Read, choose, and write.

> a frightening robot   a lovely princess   ~~a quiet giant~~   Cleo   pirate Jim

1. They keep their socks in the box.   _a quiet giant_
2. They keep their treasure in the box.   _____
3. They keep their space rocks in the box.   _____
4. They keep their necklaces in the box.   _____
5. They sleep in the box.   _____

3 Read and match. Then write for you. Compare with a friend.

1. Max and Li Mei   a) live in different countries.
2. Sato and Pablo   b) are different ages.
3. Diego and Lisa   c) are loud and quiet.
4. Uma and David   d) tell stories in different ways.

Do you have any friends who are different ages? How old are they? _____

My favorite character is _____
because _____ .

Storytellers club

Extra time?
Think about a friend. Make a list of things that are the same and different.

I can read a story about being friends with different people.

LESSON 5
Vocabulary and Grammar

1 🎧 9.2 **Listen and number. Then choose and write.**

~~frightening~~   handsome   loud   lovely   mean   quiet

a _____ ☐
b _____ ☐
c _____ ☐
d __frightening__ [1]
e _____ ☐
f _____ ☐

2 Look at 1. Read and circle.

① **Was / Were** the robots frightening?
Yes, they **was / were**.

② **Was / Were** the prince mean?
No, he **wasn't / weren't**.

③ **Was / Were** the monsters loud?
Yes, they **were / weren't**.

④ **Was / Were** the queen lovely?
No, she **was / wasn't**.

⑤ **Was / Were** the girl frightening?
No, she **was / wasn't**.

⑥ **Was / Were** the mouse loud?
No, it **was / wasn't**.

3 Imagine it's *World Book Day*. Read and complete. Then write your own questions and answers.

① ___Was___ your favorite character lovely? Yes, _____ .
_____ , but _____ loud.

② _____ the robots loud? No, _____ .
_____ frightening and _____ mean.

③ _____
_____

⏰ **Extra time?**

Write about yourself when you were a baby.
I wasn't quiet. I was loud, but I was lovely.

I can ask and answer questions about what characters were like.

LESSON 6
Listening and Speaking

1 🎧 **Listen and number.**

a   b   c   d [1]

2 **Look and complete the dialogs.**

GOLDILOCKS and the three bears

There was a young girl.

Was she lovely?

Yes, _____ .

_____ frightening?

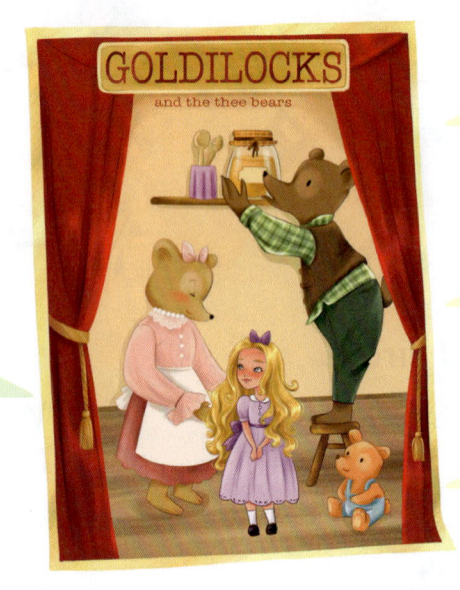

_____

_____ three bears.

_____ mean?

No, _____ .

_____

3 💬 **Choose two characters. Write two dialogs and role-play.**

Character: _____
_____
_____

Character: _____
_____
_____

Was the queen frightening?   No, she wasn't.

⏰ **Extra time?**
Tell your friend about your favorite movie. Describe the characters.

I can talk about what characters in a story were like.

LESSON 7
Myself and others
Relationship skills

Making friends

1 🎧 9.4 **Listen and circle blue for Lou and green for Zak.**

ten years old   cooking   dancing
be an actor   make movies   singing   reading
pizza   salad   eight years old

Lou   Zak

2 💡 **Think about you and a friend. Complete the diagram. Then write.**

Me
I have _____ .
My hair is _____ .
My eyes are _____ .
I like _____ .
My favorite food is _____ .

Same
We both _____ .

My friend
They have _____ .
Their hair is _____ .
Their eyes are _____ .
They like _____ .
Their favorite food is _____ .

My portfolio

3 💡 **Make a We are the same, we are different poster.**

We are the same, we are different!

This is me:

This is _____ :

We are the same:
_____ _____

We are different:
_____ _____

⭐ **Be a hero!** ⭐
Who's your favorite character in the unit? How are you the same and different?

I can make new friends and be friends with different people.

107

LESSON 8
My world

Fairy tales

1 **Read and match.**

1. characters
2. setting
3. problem
4. solution

a. This is an answer to a problem.
b. This is where a story takes place.
c. These are the people or animals in a story.
d. Something that isn't working and needs a solution.

2 **You want to write a fairy tale. Think and write.**

1. What types of characters do I put in my fairy tale? _____
2. What setting do I use? _____
3. What does the bad character usually do? _____
4. What does the good character usually do? _____
5. What type of ending do fairy tales usually have? _____

3 **Think of a traditional fairy tale. Complete the chart. Then write the fairy tale in your own words.**

The characters in my fairy tale are:	_____
The setting is:	_____
The bad character is:	_____
The good character is:	_____
The problem is:	_____
The solution is:	_____

I can read and talk about fairy tales.

Extra time?
Read your fairy tale to your friends. Can they guess the title?

A fairy tale

**LESSON 9
Project**

1 Read. Which fairy tale has a plan? Use it to complete the chart.

Fairy tale A ○
Hana was a pirate. She was mean to the queen. Johnny saves the queen. Everyone is happy in the end.

Fairy tale B ○
The queen and princess were on a spaceship. Hana the pirate was there, too. She was frightening and mean. One day, Johnny saves the queen and the princess. Everyone is happy!

Characters
Good: _____
_____
_____
Bad: <u>Hana the pirate</u>

Setting
_____

Solution
_____

Problem
_____
_____

2 Plan your fairy tale. Write. Then complete.

frightening   handsome   loud
lovely   mean   quiet

How do you start your fairy tale?
_____

What happens in the middle? _____

How do you end your fairy tale?
_____

Characters
Good: _____
_____
_____
Bad: _____
_____

Setting
_____

Problem
_____

Solution
_____

3 Reflect on your project.

I make my characters interesting and my story exciting:
☆☆☆☆☆

I write ideas for different parts of my story in different boxes:
☆☆☆☆☆

Check!
I plan my story before I write it. ○
I write a list of adjectives I can use to describe the characters in my story. ○

My fairy tale
Who's your favorite character? _____
What's your favorite part of your story? _____

I can use a plan to create a fairy tale.

**LESSON 10
Review**

My progress journal

1 Read and circle.

Our party!

Sato **1 (was)** / **were** a **2 princess** / **queen**. Cleo was **3 in a castle** / **on another planet** with Rapunzel. Uma was **4 on a pirate ship** / **in a jungle**. She was **5 loud** / **quiet** – she always makes a lot of noise. Max was a **6 mean** / **handsome** king. He was frightening. Diego was **7 an astronaut** / **a prince**. He was in a spaceship. The party was fun!

2 Read and write.

1. Was Dan in a spaceship? No, he ___wasn't___ . He _____ in a secret garden.
2. Was Jenny in a spaceship? Yes, she _____ . She _____ in a secret garden.
3. Was Jenny frightening? Yes, she _____ . She _____ quiet, too.
4. Was Dan frightening? No, he _____ frightening, but he _____ loud.

3 What I know.

Write. What's your favorite book?
Why? _____

Say. Talk about this scene from the video.
What happens? Do you like it?

Star progress

- This unit was ☆☆☆☆☆
- My favorite lesson is _____
  because _____ .
- I can now _____ .

UNIT 9
Exam practice

Listening

1 🎧 **Listen and write.**

A different fairy tale

1. The prince and princess were on their ____horses____ .
2. The prince's name was _____ .
3. They were in _____ .
4. The secret garden was near _____ .
5. Horses eat _____ .
6. The prince and princess' home was in the _____ .

Reading

2 **Look at 1. Read and write.**

Complete the sentences.

1. The prince and princess were on ____horses____ .
2. There was a tall _____ .
3. The prince was very _____ .

Answer the questions.

4. What's the princess wearing?
   _____
5. What's the prince wearing?
   _____

Write two sentences about the picture.

6. _____
7. _____

Speaking

3 💬 **Look at the pictures in 1 and in 3. Tell the story.**

The brave princess

Pearson Education Limited
KAO Two
KAO Park
Hockham Way
Harlow, Essex
CM17 9SR
England
and Associated Companies throughout the world.

pearsonenglish.com
© Pearson Education Limited 2022

© 2022 Disney Enterprises, Inc. All rights reserved.
Pixar properties © Disney/Pixar

Mr. and Mrs. Potato Head® are registered trademarks of Hasbro, Inc. Used with permission. © Hasbro, Inc. All rights reserved.
© Just Play, LLC.

The right of Catherine Zgouras to be identified as the author of this Work has been asserted by her in accordance with the Copyright, Designs and Patents Act 1988.

All rights reserved; no part of this publication may be reproduced, stored in a retrieval system, or transmitted in any form or by any means, electronic, mechanical, photocopying, recording, or otherwise without the prior written permission of the Publishers.

First published 2022
Third impression 2023
ISBN: 978-1-292-44165-8
Set in Arta Medium 17/22pt

Printed in Slovakia by Neografia

Image Credits:
123RF.com: Alena Ozerova 107, Alexgrash 48, Brian Jackson 48, Cathy Yeulet 107, Highwaystarz 45, Ilfede 24, Trodler 48; **Alamy Stock Photo:** ColourNews 48, DPA Picture Alliance 72, ImageBROKER 72, WaterFrame 96; **Getty Images:** Gary John Norman 85, Imgorthand 2, Krisana Sennok 24, Daniela Solomon 2, SolStock 45; **Shutterstock:** 794854 70, Andrey_Popov 48, Anna Nahabed 46, Artem Evdokimov 60, Be Good 48, Bonga1965 46, Boris Medvedev 48, Carlos Huang 70, Christian Bertrand 48, Dinoton 96, Eric Isselee 5, Focal Point 48, Fokke Baarssen 24, Haryigit 84, KristinaSh 108, Ku_suriuri 61, Lifestyle Graphic 11, 23, 35, 47, 48, 49, 59, 61, 71, 83, 95, 107, Maciej Oleksy 48, Mangostar 85, Mark Higgins 96, Martin Prochazkacz 96, Maximillian cabinet 72, Michael Vi 72, MIGUEL GARCIA SAAVEDRA 48, Natdive 96, Newman Studio 70, Nikola Bilic 96, Photka 10, 11, 13, 23, 25, 26, 34, 35, 37, 38, 47, 49, 50, 59, 61, 62, 71, 74, 83, 85, 86, 98,110, StudioSmart 48, Sunabesyou 59, Talvi 5, Topform 11, VanderWolf Images 24, Wavebreakmedia 85, Yegor Korzh 70.

Cover images © 2022 Disney Enterprises, Inc. All rights reserved.
Pixar properties © Disney/Pixar

Illustrations
Kay Coenen/Advocate Art pp. 25; Emily Cooksey/Plum Pudding Illustration pp. 65 (activity 4), 85; Katarina Gasko/Plum Pudding Illustration pp. 39 (activity 2), 67, 75, 93, 102 (activity 1); Isobel Lundie/Plum Pudding Illustration pp. 15, 39 (activity 1), 46, 51 (activity 2), 71 (activity 1), 81, 82, 84, 87, 94 (activity 3), 99, 104; Emanuela Mannello/Advocate Art pp. 106, 111; Irene Montano/Advocate Art pp. 27 (activity 3), 30, 42, 55, 57, 63, 78 (activity 2), 90, 94 (activity 2), 95, 105; Veronica Montoya/Advocate Art (course characters); Angelika Scudamore/Advocate Art pp. 6, 12; Miriam Serafin/Advocate Art pp. 29, 33, 34, 45, 51 (activity 3), 69; Simon Smith/Beehive Illustration pp. 66; Roger Stewart/Beehive Illustration pp. 10; Sernur Usik/Plum Pudding Illustration pp. 19, 31, 58, 73, 78 (activity 1), 91, 102 (activity 2), 103; Diego Vaisberg/Advocate Art pp. 3, 9, 11, 18, 21, 22, 23, 27 (activity 1), 36, 54, 60, 65 (activity 3), 71 (activity 3), 96.